REVERSE HEART DISEASE NATURALLY

The Woman's Guide to Not Die before Your Time

LAURIE MORSE

Difference Press

Washington, DC, USA

Published 2019

ISBN: TK

DISCLAIMER

Cover Design: Jennifer Stimson

Editor: Emily Tuttle

Author's photo courtesy of: Suzanne Hansen Ofeldt

Advanced Praise

Medical doctors are wonderful about relating biological and chemical information about the heart and its amazing connection to all parts of our body. But Laurie takes the workings of the heart in a different direction with *Reverse Heart Disease Naturally,* counseling us with step-by-step direction to heal both the muscle and the essence of our hearts. Most of us have abused our physical and ethereal hearts by poor nutrition, lackadaisical physical activity, and weak or negative thinking; as well as not mending the heart that has been broken a million times in our lives. We, as women, tend to the needs of everyone around us. Laurie asks us to take time and follow her suggestions, encouragement, and guidance to heal our hearts and bodies. I loved this book at first pass but now am reading it again with a highlighter, a pen, and notebook to study and live the wonderful lessons Laurie has imparted.

– Pam Danek, administrative assistant

I love, love, *love* Laurie Morse's *Reverse Heart Disease Naturally!* Thank you from the bottom of my heart for writing it, Laurie– so very well done!

– Joanne Kent, energy healer

Nourishment! Whether you're facing a medical challenge or just want to continue on the road to optimum health, *Reverse Heart Disease Naturally* provides important and valuable information for you. With a 'blueprint' ready to be tailored to each individual's unique place and needs on the health continuum, *Reverse Heart Disease Naturally* is filled with jewels that seem to seep into your consciousness and come through right when you need. Easy to understand, simple and concise, I highly recommend taking the journey toward more ease and health.

– Laurie Haw, executive director

I opened *Reverse Heart Disease Naturally* this morning and can't stop reading. Wow. What a gift this is for women everywhere. Laurie is lifting up important information in *Reverse Heart Disease Naturally*! The story about finding the blueprints after she meditated is phenomenal! As I read her words, my body was crying out *yes*! Her thoughts on doctors and our current medical system is so on point! Thank you, Laurie, for sharing this.

– Ally Merk, mother of three

I had no idea how much I was missing in what I do for my health. Laurie explains things so clearly and writes about the science and research in such an understandable way. I feel like she's sitting right across from me and we're having a conversation. This is really important information for everyone because it covers physical, emotional, and spiritual aspects of the heart. I've gotten it for several of my family members and friends. Thank you so much!

– Ashley Cuvetto, software developer and manager

Thank you, Laurie, for pulling together the disparate parts of the journey toward wholeness and inner peace that took me so long to discover on my own. I constantly sense your authenticity and enthusiasm, as if you were sitting at my side, patiently laying out concepts and simple practices that take me from mind to body for a profound fullness of understanding.

– Dana Ross, retired educator

Laurie's teachings go far beyond healing heart disease. Her extensive knowledge, experience, and clarity on these subjects make her just the kind of model and teacher we all could use in our lives and on our paths for more strength in our health, our choices on how we decide to live every day, and most importantly, how we decide to love ourselves and the people around us. She clearly develops a solid plan with easy-to-follow steps in a non-judgmental way for each of us to be able to start wherever we happen to be on our path.

– Michelle Abell, real estate appraiser

Reverse Heart Disease Naturally is a life map, a life saver really, for those who have lost their way with their heart health, mind, body, and Spirit (which I thought I had a handle on until reading this book). Not only does Laurie compassionately explain science and healing, she makes it easy to understand and carry into everyday life. A must read for anyone who is struggling with heart health at any level.

– Sandy Jenks, attorney

I've read a lot of books, but nothing has moved and inspired as much as *Reverse Heart Disease Naturally*. I see how healing works in ways I never did before. I'm forever grateful for these life changing insights!

– Barbara Delzwack, music teacher

To the One Power and Presence of Love. I will always serve you in deep humble gratitude for Your Wisdom, Guidance, Power, Abundance, and Love. For teaching me that You are everywhere. In everyone and everything. For teaching me to be your instrument and vessel. And for always being there, even when I forget to remember.

Eternally Grateful.

Table of Contents

FOREWORD

As a cardiologist I've observed and learned that the human heart holds our deepest powers and secrets. Even as I've spent decades saving lives with modern procedures such as angioplasty and stents, it has been my patients who have broadened my understanding of the power of holistic and integrative interventions to heal. It's not either/or, but rather, both/and.

In forming the Scripps Center for Integrative Medicine in San Diego, California which weaves the best of modern technology, nutrition, and evidence-based alternative therapies, I've watched lives become meaningful and hearts heal at deep levels with lasting impact. Heart disease is not a death sentence as much as it is a wake-up call.

Heart disease carries layers of grief and guilt, stress and love, wounds and wholeness, all looking for the healing of those layers in order to reveal the wisdom and intelligence deep in every heart. Yet, these layers don't show up on standard western tests.

There are deep stories carved into every human heart that can only be told by them. When patients tell their stories, and are heard, they literally speak their diagnosis, their personal medicine. I call this compassionate medicine.

The symptoms and risk factors of heart disease such as too high cholesterol, blood pressure, angina, are all literally the heart speaking. "Pay attention, I need help!" The research is clear that tending a human heart beyond medication and procedures is imperative for living a long healthy life.

We're at the precipice of a new paradigm of heart health, one that must consider support for a person's emotional, mental, creative, spiritual, and social well-being, as important as the hardware and medications that have been at the forefront of western medical. A both/and paradigm.

In my first book "The Heart Speaks", I write about my journey as a cardiologist and the valuable lessons I learned from my patients. My experience as Medical Director for the Ornish Program to reverse heart disease taught me that there is a physical, emotional and spiritual heart.

Laurie's book "Reverse Heart Disease Naturally" teaches the reader how to tend their stories and heal their heart at the deeper layers.

Her 7 Steps to Heart Health outline what is vital to healing your heart to wholeness. The first step of connecting with your Spirit, the Source of Life beating your heart right now is foundational to deep healing.

The next step of heart healthy nutrition is extremely important at the physical level which we know based on ample and undisputable research, yet this step also includes a perspective on nutrition from an emotional and spiritual point of view. Any time we approach something from a holistic point of view, there tends to be greater effect.

As a muscle, the heart requires movement to be healthy, and while we know "cardio" is a necessary ingredient in the exercise recipe, you'll also learn about non-exercise activity that is equally important in heart health.

The mind and its thoughts are unseen entities and yet are involved in every aspect of being human. The data shows that mind-body-spirit interventions play an important role in healing, and the active cohesion between the head and heart form a weave of connection that promotes the balance of chemical, neurotransmitter, endocrine, and whole-body communication and healing. I think it's fair to say that minding this head/heart cohesion is like a lynchpin in the equation of heart health.

I have watched people make the much-needed changes in their lives in order to live, for some it's a struggle to juggle it all. We all have the same twenty-four hours in a day, yet Laurie teaches how to access time in a different way, outside of the linear ways we've been taught, in order to navigate the changes with greater ease.

Based in ancient wisdom and tradition the heart is not only the seat of consciousness and intelligence, but also the seat of emotions. When long-held emotions of betrayal, guilt, grief, heartbreak, disappointment, and resentments have built up over a lifetime, they eventually express as dis-ease. Our stories hold the key to emotional healing. Learning to turn toward, rather than run from, our emotional landscape is a key element in healing and emotional freedom. It is possible to re-weave the energy of our emotions into qualities more akin to courage, strength, and wisdom.

Every human heart has locked inside a great well of creative energy. As you tap into this, it liberates an aspect of healing unlike any other medicine. When one intentionally directs their creative life force, it can alchemize unhealthy wounds into wholeness. It can repair brokenness, liberate love, and fill to overflowing the feeling of "not enough".

Heart disease is more often than not, treatable, and even reversible requiring your willingness to consciously be on a journey of healing. A journey that cultivates the wholeness that is already in you.

I believe that each heart has a biography, language, and method of revealing its truth, if we know how to listen.

Some of the language of the heart includes story, image, symbol, creativity, and meditation, and importantly, being witnessed. I call this compassionate medicine.

Any one on these 7 steps put you on the path to heart health, together the steps walk you into your personal medicine in order to curate health. The reason I highly recommend this journey is because I've watched over the years, with my own eyes so many people where healing happens not when motivated by fear, but rather deep caring and compassion. This book is a compassionate guide for your journey.

A "how to" on your path where you discover that Laurie really cares about your heart and healing.

She and I are aligned in that, we know that as every heart heals, the world becomes a better place, and the tapestry of humanity is strengthened. It is my hope that your thread in the tapestry be as strong and brilliant as it was designed to be.

Mimi Guarneri, MD FACC ABOIM
Pres. Academy Integrative Health and Medicine
San Diego, California

Chapter 1: If I'm So Smart, Why Can't I Figure This Out?

"The most intense conflicts, if overcome, leave behind a sense of security and calm that is not easily disturbed. It is just these intense conflicts and their conflagration which are needed to produce valuable and lasting results."

— Carl Jung

I loved the first time I heard that the body wants nothing more than to be in homeostasis. As an integrative practitioner of wholeness, that was like a first kiss. A good first kiss. As defined by Merriam-Webster, homeostasis to a body is the tendency toward a relatively stable equilibrium between interdependent elements, especially as maintained by physiological processes. That's a fancy way of saying it's how our body likes to roll.

Like Nature Herself, if she were left to her own devices, without human influence, her entire system would be in balance. Always. It's good to remember we are part of nature; we can't not be.

You may be asking yourself, "What gives? Why does it seem like I'm struggling for my life? Why is heart disease the number one killer of women over fifty, with or without family history? And if I'm so smart (and I know you are), why can't I figure this out?"

Those are some of the very reasonable questions you might be asking these days. I'd love for you to know, right off the bat, that it's not your fault. Sometimes it may feel like it is, like when you review your lab work with your cardiologist, or when you look in the mirror and see those extra pounds your doctor has highly recommended you lose, or when you choose the cake over the kale.

I get it. There seems to be a lot of dos and don'ts when it comes to not dying prematurely of heart disease. Those dos and don'ts bustle along in a fairly strong current of disease in our culture.

Let's be honest, the incentive to make people well seems to have waned over the last decades. We can point fingers to bottom-line profits in large industries — such as insurance, pharmaceutical, and even the government — that pull the strings. There's a lot more profit in unwell people than in healthy people, especially those with chronic diseases that require long term management and medication.

When you are being carried along a strong cultural current and don't realize that fact, it's not easy to change the tide, get out of the current, and find your flow.

Yet, when we consider primary function of a healthy cardiovascular system, "flow" is the point. We need blood flowing freely in vessels, in and out of an organ we call the heart, with electrical precision and timing. And when that doesn't happen, or her function falters, the body is going to get your attention asking that you make whatever adjustments necessary to regain equilibrium and homeostasis.

It's a pretty intelligent feedback mechanism, actually. A symptom is nothing more than the intelligence of the body asking for a modification in what is or isn't being done, often over a long period of time.

Almost every woman I've worked with during my thirty years in the field of Chinese medicine doesn't see her symptoms as intelligent. Quite

16

the opposite. They freak her out and drive her to google all manner of terrible possibilities, causing a cascade of stress that would drive anyone to drink.

What if your shortness of breath, fatigue, palpitations, high cholesterol, blood pressure, blood sugar imbalance, extra weight, swelling, peripheral artery disease or clogged arteries (which can be painful), insomnia, dizziness, and weakness are brilliant, intelligent messages that are getting your attention for one reason only – to save your life.

No matter your genetic predisposition, or whether you have one, two, or all of the symptoms above, there isn't a single person alive who can't reverse her current set of circumstances and live a long healthy life. You included.

Maybe you don't "feel" any symptoms right now, but you have the early warning signs in your cholesterol, blood pressure, blood sugar, or inflammation creeping up. Women don't seem to realize that any of these markers indicate heart disease. This is why doctors call heart disease a "silent" disease, in that a woman often doesn't realize she has heart disease until there's a cardiac event, such as a heart attack or stroke. Taking medication should not be the *only* way you manage your heart. Medication alone doesn't heal your damaged or hardening arteries.

If there's one thing I've learned – fortunately I've learned more than one thing – it's that the body really does want to be in balance more than anything. That's exactly what a body does when given the right support.

You may have read all the books and recommendations online about how to reverse heart disease naturally, and I imagine because you're smart, you've incorporated many of those recommendations into your life. So why haven't they moved the needle as much as you'd hoped? Why is your doctor still saying your numbers could be better? Or, if your numbers have improved, why don't you feel better?

Oh man, that's so frustrating, isn't it? And boy, do I get it. It's wildly frustrating to be willing to do what it takes but have no idea what that would be. What's "your" recipe for heart health? Why does it look like other people seemingly have it figured out? Well, first of all, "other people" wouldn't be dying of heart disease if they had it figured out.

Looking at the Costs Head-On

One person dies of heart disease every thirty-eight seconds in the US. It's the leading cause of death globally. It is also the leading cause of death for women in the United States, taking more female lives than all cancers (including breast cancer), accidents, respiratory illness, and Alzheimer's combined.

Direct and indirect costs of all cardiovascular diseases and stroke are estimated to total more than 329.7 billion dollars; that includes both health expenditures and lost productivity. Heart disease and heart attacks are two of the ten most expensive diseases treated in U.S. hospitals.

In fact, the average cost of treating a patient admitted to a hospital with a heart attack is $18,200 according to Medicare data. Unfortunately, you don't get to opt for the average charge, and if an ambulance takes you to a higher-cost emergency room for cardiology, the tab for a single heart attack could be $100,000 or more.

Of course, a single hospital admission doesn't include the cost of long-term chronic heart disease management, of which insurance covers only a portion.

On a personal level, families who experience heart disease or stroke have to deal with not only medical bills, but also lost wages and the real potential of a decreased standard of living.

Bottom line: This disease is expensive no matter how you slice it.

Unfortunately, those statistics are on the rise. So yeah, something's missing in the recipe for heart health worldwide.

Not only will your recipe save you a ton of money and time, it will literally save your life.

One Woman's Experience

Mary was a classic work-hard, independent kind of gal. She prided herself in a high work ethic, rarely dropping a ball, and often exceeding client expectations. Her staff and her bosses loved her. Unfortunately, all that over-drive service she provided was for everyone but herself. Her family got what she had left after a long day, leaving nothing for her.

She never even thought about this until she hit midlife. She was riding the wave of success and paid no attention to anything else. She had whispers here and there that asked her to take better care of herself. She set those requests aside until the whispers turned into screams.

There's a quote from the Buddha that says, "If your compassion doesn't include yourself, it is incomplete."

In Mary's case, her work standards and pride of taking great care of everyone around her didn't include herself. Thus, it was incomplete.

When the whispers turned to screams, it was almost too late. Mary had a heart attack during a particularly stressful and challenging family situation involving financial strain. She almost died. While she was in the hospital, she was stunned to learn the dire statistics about women and heart disease, and unbeknownst to her, she had been racking up the markers since her last visit to her doctor. Her blood pressure was high. She'd gained another twenty pounds that she was always trying to lose.

She regularly had heart flutters that she brushed off and told no one about prior to her heart attack.

She was scared. She hated that her daughters witnessed her heart attack, her collapse, the ambulance emergency, surgery for a stent (well, they didn't "see" the surgery, but it was terrible for them to not know if their mom would live as they paced the family waiting room for two hours). The whole family was scared. No one cared one bit how much it cost to save their mom and wife's life; no cost was too high. They had to face that music later.

Mary couldn't see or hear her body's calls for attention before the heart attack. But afterward, and to Mary's great credit, she woke up and tended to expanding her consciousness and made some really amazing healing strides. Together we put together her recipe, and she whipped that dish up regularly and can now proudly say that she's reversed all her risk factors and feels better than she did twenty years ago.

Now Mary trusts her body. She doesn't feel terrorized by every little thing she feels, nor does she ignore it. She creates her days differently than she did before. She doesn't leave her heart center for the lures of distraction. She realizes there are many distractions, but none worth her life. I'll pull back the curtain for more of Mary's average days as we keep moving forward.

Mostly Mary feels alive and healthy and excited that she'll be around for her daughters' marriages, milestones, and grandbabies (that she looks forward to cuddling). She and her husband have gotten closer, which is something she's very grateful for. They had grown apart over the last years, and she didn't realize how much her heart ached because of that. She didn't know what to do about it, and honestly didn't feel like she had time to deal with it. She no longer sweeps things under the carpet. She now has creative ways of navigating the flow of her life.

Looking Deeper into Heart Health

I love the notion that things are "hidden in plain sight." Then once you "see" them, it seems so obvious. I've thought about this a lot in regard to heart health. To start, I had to ask myself, "Why? Why do the wealthiest countries have the poorest heart disease statistics? Why is it the number one killer in women over fifty?"

You might already have your own thoughts, but I'm not going to say it's because of the wealth, or the fatty steaks and booze-filled dinners that wealth can buy. It doesn't help the situation, but it's not what I've discovered to be the lynchpin.

What I've discovered are some vital ingredients to a heart health recipe that few even address. Yes, it's important to eat whole foods, and we'll talk about that and more in the nutrition chapter. Yes, it's imperative to move your body for cardiovascular health, and we'll talk about that too. But I had to dig deeper. It took a while to find the treasure, but I did find it, and you'll get the scoop on all that treasure as we journey through these pages together. You'll also learn how to weave it into your world so you can live your natural design of a long, healthy life.

As we know, a recipe is made up of particular ingredients. If some of those ingredients are left out, the intended recipe doesn't work. A simple message hidden in plain sight. If as many as half of heart disease cases aren't able to be linked to traditional risks such as family history, obesity, high blood pressure, cholesterol, sugar, smoking, or too little activity, then what other ingredients are we missing?

21

And for the half that can be linked to the traditional risks, we *know* heart disease is reversable. So then why isn't that happening more? Why isn't death by heart disease on the decline instead of on the rise?

If a woman at risk made specific changes, she could literally change her risk markers within three weeks. If she kept that up, she could absolutely keep her *Titanic* from hitting the iceberg.

If one person has done the thing we want to do successfully, then it's possible for anyone else to do it too. There have been times when I've had to hang on to that thread of truth like a lifeline, a nail biter of a scene that didn't let me bite my nails because my hands were holding on so tight. But, it ended well. And it will for you too.

It's important to create a dish with all the ingredients, wouldn't you agree? Seriously, who doesn't love a good sweet potato pie in the fall? Well, it's not a sweet potato pie without the sweet potatoes. There's no way around it, we've gotta have the sweet potatoes for a sweet potato pie.

Throughout these pages, we're going to create your recipe for heart health together. And you're going to make a commitment to yourself to use all the ingredients. You are a gourmet meal. Period. You deserve the best quality ingredients and *all* the ingredients in the creation of your heart health. That's how much I believe in you. Why would I say that if I haven't even met you? Because if you're reading this book and it found its way to you, then I believe this material is meant for you, and ipso facto, I believe in *you*.

There is an ancient tradition in many cultures involving a Red Thread. A Red Thread represents love, blood (important in our heart, vessel, blood conversation), passion, and connection. In particular, when two people connect, the ancient wisdom of the Red Thread says that they are meant to meet and connect. That they are on each other's thread.

You are on my Red Thread because your heart has a message for you, a message you will find on these pages, and we're now officially connected.

I invite you to remember the part about you being a gourmet meal. Not a fast-food, chain, gourmet wannabe. You, your loved ones, and your life are gourmet creations, and worth the time and attention it takes to curate that creation consciously.

There's a secret ingredient to how healing really works that we could consider, in this gourmet analogy, to be like the binder. The ingredient that holds it all together as you stir and add and scrape out your mixture into the baking or serving dish. You will soon know that secret ingredient. I suggest you keep plenty in stock.

Yes, all the ingredients in the recipe you and I are talking about are natural. But in case you're wondering about what to do about your medications and less natural means of heart support, we can't know that straight away. You will know what to do as your blood markers, pressure, and sugar levels give you the life affirming feedback of improvement.

Only then can we decide how to proceed. I will tell you, it's exciting to get off one blood pressure medication, then the other, and maintain excellent pressure by way of your own cellular intelligence.

Integrative support is meant to be an adjunct to your primary medical support. Make no decisions that aren't thoughtfully considered and discussed with your heart health team.

Did you know that the blueprint for perfect health lives in every cell of your being? In the correct environment, every cell would be expressing that equilibrium of health and wholeness. That's the environment you'll be creating on this heart health journey. That's how heart disease gets "reversed," and that's how you prevent premature death by stroke or heart attack.

The heart happens to be a perfect symbol for the flow of life energy. Life energy is creative in nature. Anatomically, the heart is a hollow muscular structure that functions as the primary organ of the circulatory system and maintains the circulation of the blood throughout a network of vessels. The circulation of blood is essential, as it carries the oxygen and nutrients to cells, organs and muscles to function, and removes byproduct and waste. Thus, the heart and the blood it pumps maintains and sustains life in a body.

Life is precious. Life is a force. A gift. Life is something we tend and create. Life asks of us to choose it, or it shall be taken.

I'm glad you made the decision to take this journey. You won't be disappointed. Rather, you'll liberate your inner intelligence (see, we know you are smart), and that's how you'll live the long, healthy life you so deserve.

Be the woman who is free from her diagnosis. Your diagnosis doesn't own you.

Chapter 2: From Frustration to Freedom

"Every human has four endowments - self-awareness, conscience, independent will, and creative imagination. These give us the ultimate human freedom... The power to choose, to respond, to change."

— Stephen Covey

In my meditations back in mid-2007, I was asking to understand the true nature of health and wholeness. This became a burning desire to understand, because I had just spent the last twenty years as an integrative practitioner of Chinese medicine in the high hopes that accessing the body's natural intelligence through acupuncture, herbs, nutrition, therapeutic breathing, and managing Qi would have gotten people, myself included, further along than it did. I felt stymied and frustrated.

One particular early summer day, as I was meditating during a lunch break, I received the information that encoded in every cell is a *"blueprint"* for health and wholeness. As I often do, I then asked, "Well then, why is there so much rampant disease which causes the feeling of being stuck, wounded, and broken?" And immediately I received the response, "Because human beings aren't yet aware that, as they consciously ask for this Divine Blueprint to become activated, it will remain dormant. With wholeness lying dormant, disease becomes a stronger force than health."

At the time, I was working in an office building that had a lovely neighborhood to walk through. After this meditation, I decided to take a twenty-minute spin around the hood and contemplate and integrate this information. As I turned the first corner, right there on a bank of ice plant that butts up against my office building, was a set of blueprints. Just lying there, impossible for me to miss. As I picked them up, I knew instantly that they were a confirmation of what had just been brought to my awareness … there is a Divine Blueprint for Wholeness in every cell.

Immediately, my logical mind was assessing the source of these blueprints. There was no construction happening anywhere nearby. I'd been in that building and neighborhood for over six years, and I knew there wasn't a single architect or contractor within miles, and definitely not in the office building I occupied. What I then heard was, "These are for you. They are to confirm the importance of teaching people not only that there *is* such a thing as a 'blueprint for wholeness encoded in every cell' but how important it is to activate it."

I spent the next several years frozen and freaked out about this. I kept it completely to myself, not wanting to admit I might have to step up and defend a wholeness that is almost one-hundred percent contradictory to the current mainstream medical system. Who was I to go against such a powerful system? It took me quite a while to make peace with the idea that I don't have to "go against" anything. Rather, I could put forward the truth and allow those who wanted to take themselves on this path to step forward. As I did that with myself and others, results were stunning.

I still have those blueprints. They serve as a reminder of one of the first steps to real healing, which is to accept the idea that encoded in every single cell is a Divine Design, a perfect blueprint and pattern for health and wholeness. I would go on to excitedly learn that we have approximately 37.2 trillion cells, and in every single cell, there are approximately 37.2 trillion atoms. Within every atom is an electron which carries the blueprint *and* instructions for how to awaken the healing light in these electrons. If you think about it, that's a lot of freaking wholeness. I can't even do that math, but it's obvious that it's *way* more wholeness than any of the maladies almost anyone has.

I would spend the next ten years weaving together the research, ancient wisdom, spiritual truths, the intelligent understanding of how a body works through the eyes of Chinese medicine, and my own applied experience.

As I said in the last chapter, there is a recipe for activating the blueprint in our cells. It is most definitely a "thing!" In this book, I will invite you to dive into and learn how to do this for yourself.

I was one of those women who didn't feel any symptoms, but still my cholesterol, inflammation, and blood sugar began creeping up. I was quite shocked actually, because I considered myself to be very healthy. I'm a health care provider after all, it's my job to be healthy! I take the proverb "physician, heal thyself" to heart.

I could never, in my integrity, be a steward of health for others if I weren't "practicing what I preach." It's a problem in medicine right now that many doctors, nurses, and providers are unwell. That's a disconnect, in my view.

Because I have both heart disease and diabetes in my family history, I got busy doing everything in this book. The results were that all my markers reversed, I'm on no medications at all as I approach sixty years old, and I feel very good.

Only after treating myself and scores of other women did I feel integrity about writing this love letter to you about your heart health.

A Conscious Heart

Did you know that the heart has her own consciousness, and that this consciousness is connected to the Source of Life? It sort of makes sense if you think about it. The heart has her own electrical system referred to as a natural pacemaker, sending out regular electrical impulses that control the heart rate and send electrical signals through the heart muscle, which causes the heart to contract and then pump blood throughout the entire body.

Simply put, all this electrical signaling from brain to heart and body is an electron dance that involves further impulses from outside our own body. We are not a closed system. The exchange of air, the food we eat, the connection to other people and nature all influence our electronic force all day every day.

When a heart is struggling to function well, our first order of business is to bring equilibrium to our system. For the sake of you and I being on the same page, I'll refer to our "system" as the mental, emotional, physical, and spiritual bodies operating in harmony *and* in dynamic balance with nature and environment. My intelligent heart and system taught me what it needed to heal. This dance or exchange is not static, but rather quite dynamic. Learning how to dance in this dynamic flow is like learning to fish, in the analogy of it's good to give a person a fish, but better to teach them how to fish.

Barbara came in one day upset because her chest was very tight, she could hardly take a deep breath, and she was scared. She had been driving home from a visit to her daughter the weekend before and noticed this chest pain. She said it felt "crushing." She'd gone to her doctor the day after returning and before coming to see me, and they determined everything was OK, which didn't explain her experience. Being a nurse, she was well aware of how many women over fifty are taken out by way of a heart "event." She wasn't ready for that. She adores her grandchildren. Not to mention that she feels like she's finally at a place where she can focus more on herself and what she'd like to be doing. Arriving at this place after years of taking care of others seemed to inevitably leave her last. And now, she's got her family history of high blood pressure and cholesterol staring her in the face along with something crushing her heart.

She tries to eat healthy, she does, but sometimes her rebellious streak prevails because, after a long day, she really just wants the joy of her favorite foods. If only those foods could be "heart healthy," she often finds herself lamenting.

Together we employed her "recipe," her game plan, and her reason for being willing to go for it. That day, I also gave Barbara an acupuncture treatment and her crushing chest pain was completely gone by the time she left.

I love acupuncture for regulating heart function because, in part, it's an electrical medicine. When a needle of metal quality is inserted into wells of Qi or points on the body, it activates an electrical charge that conducts along the specific channel. It's a very specific message of intelligence to a specific organ.

I've learned over the years in working with hundreds of women that acupuncture is an excellent ingredient, but it's also not a main ingredient. It's one of those "can add if desired." Here's why I say that: if you're making a quiche, you've gotta have eggs, milk (dairy or non-dairy), salt, pepper, usually cheese. Then you can add spinach or ham or scallions, if that's something you want.

On the one hand, acupuncture can help a person stay on track. On the other hand, I've noticed that some people use regular treatments as way to avoid doing some of the other important heart health requirements. I can almost read their minds, "I'm doing this great thing for myself regularly, so surely I don't need to kick my nutrition up a notch, or move daily, or tend to my stress. I mean, look at how relaxed I am after every treatment."

The powerful relaxation that accompanies an acupuncture treatment is amazing, I know that, but it isn't always strong enough to last through the tsunami of stressful situations an average life has until the next treatment. Homework is required.

What if one of the reasons heart disease is on the rise is because our hearts are begging for our attention? That was certainly true for me as I listened to my own heart to heal, and she had a lot to share.

In Chinese medicine, the heart is the seat of consciousness. Consciousness is like the word "system," in that it has layers and connections. When we consider our brain, most of us think of the organ in our head, and that's not incorrect of course, but it's also more than that.

Consciousness is an awareness of self and the world. An awareness of the connection of life. The oneness of life. All that lives in the heart center. Is tending consciousness one of the requests of the heart? I'm coming to learn that it is.

The Rough Seas of Menopause

Back in the beginning of menopause, when, unbeknownst to myself, a wild ride was preparing to ensue, I had this unrelenting right shoulder pain. Hips and shoulders seem to speak out along the menopausal march for a lot of women. As a healthcare provider, I'm aware of the bountiful buffet of healing options, and as you might imagine, I tried them all for my shoulder. Nothing. A year passed, another year, still nothing. One day I was so frustrated, I sat on my bed, put my hand on my heart and asked what I was missing in getting rid of this pain.

When I ask these kind of heartfelt questions in the spirit of trusting that I live in a dynamic exchange between my own system and life herself, and that life is for me, not against me, I always get a response. It's sometimes right away, but not always. It might be a day or so later, and it could pop into my awareness through a song, something I read, or someone I overhear talking. But it always comes.

What unfolded in my awareness as I asked about my shoulder with my hand over my heart was so cool. I saw how the level of my shoulder and heart were the same, and that I was trying to fix my shoulder but the pain wouldn't go away until I got this message of intelligence from my higher consciousness, which was this, "It's time to love more."

Right away I thought, "I'm a loving person. What does that mean?" While feeling indignant in no small amount, I might add.

31

It would take a couple of years, and counting, to unfold the meaning of that message. In hindsight, the message was right on. Just because I was a good and loving person, it didn't mean I was operating from the fullness that is Love. The very same Love that happens to be the entire fabric of the Universe. Oh no, I had plenty of pockets and storage spaces (small, medium, and large) that I was hiding from Love, that I felt completely justified in holding separate from Love so I could continue my righteous judgment.

I knew of course, that Love doesn't judge. That Love heals all. That Love is the substance of life. That Love is bigger than me, and I was thirsty and didn't know it. I'd been drinking from the barely-there trickle from a spigot when there was a waterfall awaiting my attention. A waterfall that flowed freely into a river that found her way to the great body of water we know as the ocean.

As Rumi so aptly said, "Love is the bridge between you and everything."

I thought I knew love, but I only knew her pale outline. My shoulder was calling me home. I listened for a little while and then let it slip away, until I came face to face with my own heart problems a year or so later.

The markers for metabolic syndrome and heart disease, which I mentioned are on both sides of my family, were heading upward like the mercury rising in a thermometer. The kicker was, I thought I was healthier than anyone I knew. All my doctors told me I was the picture of health. Healthy diet, regular exerciser, no medications, regular meditator for years. So why couldn't I figure out why?

Epigenetics – An Emerging Branch of Science

I knew that epigenetics determined the expression, or not, of genetic predispositions. So what was I missing?

The NIH has an elegant way of describing epigenetics: "The cell epigenome is dynamic and can be affected by genetic and environmental factors. Furthermore, epigenetic modifications can be reversible, which makes the genome flexible to respond to environmental changes such as nutrition, stress, toxicity, exercise, and drugs. Stress is an important environmental factor."

Epigenetics is great news, because it means our fate isn't limited to our congenital history. This news helped me trust I wasn't doomed by my genes. We can employ what the research of epigenetics teaches us in order to keep certain genes from expressing. People are doing this all the time to change the course of their body toward health and keep the expression of hereditary genes off. It's like this: just because I have an ex-boyfriend, doesn't mean I have to invite him to my wedding.

I wouldn't have considered myself "stressed," per se. I'd long stopped waking up to an alarm (which I consider to be more like an assault), engaged in work I love, had (and still have) a loving marriage, good friends, etc.

But there was a hidden truth. A cultural auto-pilot of living in a stress response virtually all day every day. For many, even all night long. So insidious that it no longer even feels like stress, it feels like the new normal. It's the way it is. And there's only one way out of this trap, which you will discover as we journey through these pages.

It turns out that I hadn't yet employed "the recipe" with myself. Not completely, anyway. I promise that by the time you finish this book, you'll know "the recipe." Everything will be laid out for you. But until I can get there, I have to ask you to bear with me!

Let's just say that I've reversed all those markers and am in full-swing prevention of premature death due to heart disease. I felt like Barbara. I wasn't ready to go yet. I'll take wisdom over youth any day and I want a long healthy life where I can apply that wisdom, expand Love as much as I possibly can, and feel good while doing it. That's my version of thriving.

While most are barely surviving the rough waters of heart disease, our design is to thrive. With the heart as a messenger, I listened and was taken on a journey that guided me to thrive. Those who listen will be taken on a journey that unquestionably guides you to thrive.

Making Claim to the Birthright of Health

My first stop was to *claim my birthright* of health. Period. Even in the face of what appears otherwise, if you've never claimed this birthright with your whole being, then it can't be yours until you do, even if you have no idea what that means or what to do yet. Every human being must make the decision that causes providence to respond to you personally because you made the decision to claim what is rightfully yours. I could feel that happen inside of me when I claimed my birthright of health at a whole new level.

Willingness is a big component of this journey to heart health. It's the flavor of willingness that helps us keep moving along, not give up, and cultivate and tend to wholeness as it fills in little by little, surging from each and every cell. Because it's already there.

The small mind of a human being and the heart mind aren't the same. The small mind needs facts and evidence, while the heart just knows. The heart knows and is thrilled to go on the journey to wholeness with you. She's with you every step of the way.

The small mind is wildly impatient and considers the idea of a "journey" to be waste of time, unnecessary, and ridiculous. If the small mind gives in the slightest, mostly from a mocking, can't wait to say "I told you so" stance, it's only because this part of us is quite unrealistic.

She wants to flip a switch and have it all be better in a flash. She sees no journey needed.

It's the expectation of flipping a switch and it all being OK that takes us out every time. Why? Because it just doesn't work that way. It's one foot in front of the other, sometimes we're walking during lovely warm light-filled days, but other times, it's darker, but always, always every forward step gets us there.

It takes courage to journey, and yet it's filled with magic and miracles. The kind of miracle like, "Oh my gosh, my mind has settled down, and is actually listening to my heart. And my heart, she has so much bounty, she's always right, never waivers, has endless love for me and for all of life through me! Show me more, please."

My beloved heart, are you telling me that heart disease is no longer needed for me?

Yes, I am telling you that, in part because you're eating more kale, but mostly because we are in a creative, loving partnership now, which changes everything. Can you feel the ease in your body? Even as you've stopped needing your blood pressure medication to keep at bay the crazy internal tension you had. You're doing beautifully. Keep walking.

It is most assuredly your heart, not your head, that will keep you making the aligned choices so you can live a long, healthy life. It is your heart that will teach you that disease and decline are not meant to be understood as inevitable truth. Rather, the activating of your birthright is a spiritual truth that is yours to claim.

Chapter 3: Your Roadmap for Success

"To dare is to lose one's footing momentarily. To not dare is to lose oneself."

— Søren Kierkegaard

Imagine we're going on a walking tour in France, our own version of the Camino. Your very own pilgrimage to your heart. With your heart. For your heart. Because of your heart.

There will be villages to stop and see, wine to sip at sunset, fellow pilgrims to meet and share special moments with. Laces to replace. Dips in fresh waterfalls to take. Hostel cots and boutique hotel featherbeds to collapse into each night. Sunrises to be in awe of. And sweeping strokes of beauty you'll never forget. Ever.

My client Mary went on a river cruise in the canals of France with her family. It was amazing. Mary's were the best vacation pictures I've ever seen. I still have visions of the French cheese platters that were a regular part of their meals.

She described it as epic. The break was good too, but only a few months after her epic experience, she was back in full swing at work, as stressed as ever. That's when I got her e-mail that she'd had a heart attack, stent surgery, and that she was petrified.

We spent months working through the steps outlined in this chapter, and if you're willing to do the same, you can reverse your heart disease. Or any disease, for that matter. You'll be able to wake up every day not defining yourself as a ticking time bomb, but rather trusting your body to carry you through the design of a long, healthy life.

Have you ever been told that the medicine lives in the wound? It does. Your personal medicine is in your heart. And your heart, she wants you to access the medicine. She has much to share with you, and as I've mentioned, a symptom or disease is an intelligent message from our body looking to get our attention. Looking to guide us back to center, homeostasis, or balance. The thing is, we have to listen.

Coeur is the French word for heart. It's also the root of the word courage. It takes courage to listen to and live from our heart. When you do, it causes the release of biochemical signals that heal. And when you keep listening, over time, it adds up to the reversal of the disease.

Healing does not happen by matching the right drug with the ill. It happens by reversing the energy that caused the ill in the first place. Often called "getting to the root of the problem," which our culture doesn't like very much because we want the quick fix.

I've watched a tug-of-war intensify just in the last three decades. It started much earlier, but I started paying close attention about thirty years ago. The tug-of-war goes like this:

The patient says, "Doc, I don't feel well, is there something you can give me to make it go away?"

Doc knows that there's only six minutes left for this visit, doesn't really know this person other than what's in the chart, is trying to avoid doling out medication without reason, so what to do? What to do? Doc's head is spinning for the best option here. Doc really cares, but is trapped in a tight system that requires a solution.

Patient is scared, doesn't know where else to turn, and just wants to make the pain go away. This is the only signal the doc can hear from patient.

Doc is busy, patient pushes doc for a solution. Doc doesn't have time for much else. "Sure, let's give this medication a try and see how it goes," says doc.

Patient leaves feeling somewhat hopeful. Fingers crossed that this does the trick and flips the switch that makes the problem go away.

Doc's fingers are crossed too.

That's not healing. Not even close.

I talk with people all day long who are frustrated because they can't get what they need from the medical system. If they need life-saving measures, there's no better place to be than in this system. But what about all the messages of intelligence that were whispers before the screaming message that is a heart attack?

Can heart attacks be avoided if the whispers are given proper attention? I think so. Actually, I know so.

Doctors used to know their patients for years. They watched them grow, knew their family, what they did for a living, and their general temperament. Knowing those things are vital to medical decision-making. That doctor/patient relationship is no longer the norm.

What we've got now is a system that relies first on hard data (lab and blood work, MRIs biopsies, etc.) and has little time for the periphery of the person. Yet that periphery, more often than not, holds valuable clues for treatment and personal medicine for that individual.

As conventional medicine continues to advance, bringing that aspect back into the fold of treatment is a must for greater effect.

So, here's what I see and offer to the frustrated ones.

Clarity on Who Does What

Conventional medicine is a disease management system. In general, it's not a preventative system. It tries here and there, but that's not the prime directive of the system. Love it or hate it, that's just how it is currently.

Going to the doctor and expecting to have conversations about prevention or alternative options for deeper healing would be akin to going to the hairdresser and expecting them to overhaul a broken transmission. It's illogical, and we wouldn't have that expectation of our hairdresser.

This is the reason the use of alternative and integrative options continues to rise. People need to be heard, they need to know they have a partner in health. They'd like to explore that periphery and options beyond medication.

There are seven steps that I have found to be extremely comprehensive in reversing heart disease, preventing other potential health problems, and guiding people to a sense of well-being that traverses mind, body, and Spirit.

The mind, body, Spirit thing has become a bit of a cliché over the years, yet there's deep wisdom in that cliché.

Our thoughts and emotions (consciousness), body (physical function including the constant interchange with our environment), and Spirit (connection to the natural flow of life) are the foundation from which health is supported or not. It's simple, yet not always easy to find the right rhythm amid busy schedules, tucked away emotional hurts, and toxins in our air, water, and food.

In general, bodies are resilient. So we don't have to fix everything overnight, but we do need to be willing to look under all the rocks and not ignore the ones we're afraid of. I've learned that the fear of what's under the rock is worse than what's actually under the rock. Every time.

The way I look at it is this: you and I have the rest of our life to lift the rocks, make the necessary changes, and change the course of our health and life. Only an unwillingness to take the journey, listen to our heart, lift the rocks, follow the wisdom of the heart will be the problem. Unwillingness equals roadblock. Willingness equals an open road.

So let's talk about your roadmap, shall we? This roadmap is what will activate the blueprint of health in your cells. It will awaken the healing intelligence that's available in any given moment for you to consciously choose.

Step 1 – Your State of the Union

Here you will discover where you are in the "current" that is heart disease and statistics, and then pan back somewhat in order to find a broader perspective that helps you to know that reversing your heart problem is possible. You will also be shown why it's not your fault that heart health is a challenge, *and* that you have more resources than you've been able to see at your fingertips to begin reversal and lifetime prevention.

Step 2 – Getting a Grip on Nutrition

In general and across the board, nutrition is the primary topic for reversing heart disease. Yes, it's important, and there's more to it than just eating more vegetables and fruit. You'll learn how to align yourself with the best nutrition for heart health, including supplements and sleep. As a spirit-centered woman, you'll have plenty of "aha" moments as we align you, food, and Spirit. In addition, we'll cover how to successfully weave changes into your daily life with little deprivation, I promise.

Step 3 – Would You Like to Dance?

Bodies like to move, that much we know. As we gather our years and wisdom, it's not fun to force and push our body to do something she's not into. You'll be introduced to movement choices that bring you joy rather than seeing it as a chore to dread.

Step 4 – Cohesion in the Mind

Just like the heart is the center point in our body, this step is a crux, if you will, to integrating all the steps into your life. Without this, failure seems a constant companion. Here we'll talk about how a human mind works, and you'll understand the science and implications of operating from a "closed system" in your mind versus connection to the whole. The heart is a system of wholeness, and she's asking you to curate your consciousness to this truth.

Step 5 – The Ticking of Time

If you could change your relationship with time, would that be amazing? If you were no longer a victim of time but instead the boss of time, how cool would that be? We'll also talk about how to manage your energy better, and a practice for mastery over the constant judgment of self and others.

Step 6 – Is Your Heart Broken?

By the time we reach midlife, we've been heartbroken numerous times. Not just by lovers, but by things that mattered very much going awry.

You will discover how long held fears, unresolved trauma and resentments create "knots" in the heart, diminishing healthy heart function. Even as world affairs are heart breaking, the affairs of the world will be difficult to change without the wisdom, intelligence, and right actions of more and more hearts. I hope you decide to be one of those hearts.

Step 7 – Creative Healing to the Rescue!

Here we learn how to untangle those knots in the heart. You will learn the benefits of engaging with the Creative Life Force that is beating your heart and pumping your blood this very moment. Engaging with this Life Force is statistically as powerful as meditation, and while I love meditation, some women don't, so here's a pretty great alternative where you'll discover how to release emotions and cultivate a deeper connection with the wisdom and intelligence of your heart. You'll experience the magic of alchemy that happens during a creative healing process.

You can take one step at a time or you can jump to the step that needs the most attention. Whatever you do, *don't* skip any steps, especially Step 7.

Step 7 is *Creative Healing to the Rescue!* At this point, it probably doesn't feel this way, but by the time you get there, you'll really get that it's the *piece de resistance* which will help you not only potentiate the other steps, but tie them together in a coherent manner.

If you're a woman who journals, I'd get a journal that you can devote specifically to this journey. If you're familiar with mixed-media journals, I'd get one of those too. And grab some watercolor pencils while you're at it, as I'll teach a cool "disappear the tangled knot" trick.

If none of that is your thing, pen and paper will be just fine.

I'm a fan of giving the left, analytical brain some meat to chew on. She won't be very cooperative if she doesn't understand the why and what. That being said, we've got to give her these gifts, so as we move forward, gifts for your left brain, right brain, heart, and Spirit will be woven together. We won't leave anybody out.

Lastly, go through these steps more than once. It's repetition that integrates new things. Give the Seven Step Failproof Heart Health Journey a minimum of ninety days. Yes, you can literally change your heart health markers in as little as three weeks, but getting to the root takes longer. Cells turn over every ninety to 120 days, so asking for major changes before that just isn't fair to your efforts. You can always adjust along the way and redirect after ninety days, but you just can't jump ship before the ninety days.

Every organ in the body can regenerate, but only if we give our cells new signals. You will be changing the messaging to your cells in these seven steps to such a degree that, when cells turn over, they are healthier than the cells they are replacing. Replacing unhealthy cells with healthier cells day after day makes for new, up-leveled organ function.

When I realize I need to make a change, and that it's not a one-and-done, nor is it a temporary change, but rather a lifestyle change, I absolutely must make it fun or I just won't stick with it. I invite you to be in an ongoing inquiry with yourself and your heart on this journey that goes something like, "How can I make this or that more joyful? What else can I tend to here to make it more fun? What's the best way for me to receive a solution for (fill in the blank)? What else would make this something I could do consistently?"

These open inquiries are powerful.

If you bring your whole heart to this journey, you will reverse the heart disease that's temporarily gotten your attention for the intelligence it wishes to impart to you. You will no longer fear your medical future. You'll save a boatload of precious resources such as time, energy, and money, and you'll live a long, healthy life.

Shall we move along to our first step?

Chapter 4: Your State of the Union

"Love is the bridge between you and everything."
— Rumi

"What do you worry the most about?" I asked my client Marta.

"I'm so worried that I'll leave my children motherless. That would break my heart, no pun intended! Puns are usually meant to be funny," Marta said through tearful eyes.

I really appreciate Marta's sense of humor. She often jokes about her plight, which helps her let off some steam. I've also observed it's a bit of a protective mechanism.

"I want to live a long healthy life because I've worked so hard all my life, and I want time to enjoy, to slow down, travel, and hold my grandbabies. If I get cheated of that, I'll be upset."

"I completely understand," I said to Marta. I could sense she was chewing on something else, so I asked her if there was anything more.

"For a while now, I've had this, oh, I don't know … I'm not sure how to even put it into words … this 'thing' inside of me that feels like there's something more or something else. Like another part, or more of me that wants to come out before I die. Honestly, I don't know how else to explain it. It probably doesn't even make sense."

"Oh, it does," I said, "it makes total sense, and I get it that it's not easy to put into words."

Being an extension of the Creative Life Force, literally because we can't not be, that Life Force is a continuous, never-ending impulse for creating more of Itself.

From the time we're born, that impulse is unfolding. We only notice it as somewhat uncomfortable or even painful if we're stuck in a holding pattern of "less than who we really are." It's like holding the flow of a river back; it's hard to do and can have painful consequences.

What Marta was describing was likely the next version of herself ready to emerge or blossom, but something was holding this version back from surfacing naturally. We were infants who became toddlers, then children, then young adults, mothers, businesswomen. We're dynamic beings always becoming more than our current selves.

Beyond the imperative to procreate and keep the species propagated, our prime directive, our true purpose as a human being, is to become who we really are. It is to live into our Wholeness of Love embodied. This individual act is life and world changing.

I have observed over the years that there comes a time when Love has knocked softly for so long that she must resort to banging on the door so you can hear her.

I'm not talking about romantic love. I'm talking about the Love that is the entire fabric of the Universe. Divine Love, Spirit, Source, Creative Life Force, The Field, atomic energy, God, Qi, I AM Presence, call it what feels right in your heart, but call It you must.

My heart, your heart, everybody's heart is the motherboard for Love, the great director of the symphony of your being. When there is a physical disharmony within the heart, that means there is a request for greater harmony with Love, for greater harmony with your Divinity.

46

When we heed this message, then harmony automatically corrects the physical disharmony.

The heart wants what the heart wants. This can't be ignored. Period.

Our body and our heart are "electric." The heart has an electrical impulse that regulates her function and the flow of blood in and out, creating a symphonic, rhythmic harmony. It's beautiful music. Like an ultrasound of an embryo's heartbeat. Even Earth Herself has Her own music that has been detected in Her magnetic field.

Beats and rests are what create music, the symphony of our heart, and the pulse of life on Earth.

"Is that why I sometimes go into a fibrillation?" asked Marta.

"Exactly," I responded. "The motherboard is seeking harmony. Do you remember when I asked you what your spiritual stance was, and instantly you said, 'Well, I'm not religious if that's what you're asking!'"

"I do remember. I thought it was a random question, but now I love learning what an important question it actually is," Marta said.

"Right! You got a little tense and didn't really want to talk about it. But here's the thing, I see this all day long with women who consider themselves to be Spirit-centered – being spiritual is a place to stand that isn't religious because they've made the decision that religion doesn't serve them at this point. Totally cool, but there's much more to living into that choice."

Religion continues to work for plenty of people, and that's great. My mom is a devout Catholic and has never missed a week of mass in her entire life, almost eighty years. I can feel her prayers, and it was her devotion that helped me discover my own spiritual roots, and subsequently create a foundation and Union with Love, which is a never-ending work in progress.

47

We don't need to talk about the errors and mistakes that religions and various spiritual paths have made over the centuries. What is important is that when you peel back all assertions by man into the doctrine and dogma, the essence of every path is this Truth: life is Love. All is Love. You are Love. Every particle of energy is Love. There can be none other than this truth. Furthermore, Love is never sick or lacking in any way.

Living as a Spirit-centered woman means basically releasing the false and inviting the true. Exchanging density for light. Beats and rests, you can make music out of your journey if you so wish.

"So what do I do with that in my everyday life?" Marta asked.

In order to do anything with it, we have to talk about the number one wound that runs you and every human being. You need to become aware of it so you can pivot to what is true about you.

The Core Wound

The wound is this: before choosing to individualize as Source, or incarnating into your current physical life, being one with Source was warm and cozy, light-filled, and yummy. Leaving that all-encompassing soup of Source, in the instant of our incarnation, felt a bit harsh in comparison. Cold, separate, dark. Our "point of view" changed. We lost perspective.

The perception of being separate from Source is the first and core wound for a human being. What ensues after birth is a life of bouncing between fleeting feelings of connection with Source, varying degrees of suffering depending on how distant we become from Source, and everything in between.

As we grow up, we become more conscious, aware, and trained in the ways of the outside world. Because of this wound of perceived separation, the feeling of unworthiness grows as well. Why? Because a mind that perceives it is separate from the Source of all Life will try to both find and prove its worth, which is completely futile.

We'll talk about cohesion in the mind soon, and it'll make more sense as to how this plays out. Until then...

Worth in the external world will never be found.

Attempts to prove worthiness separated from Source are ignorant, arrogant, and impossible.

We can see the uncountable, multitude of ways this wound gets played out in life.

Give me a little latitude to do a broad brushstroke to say that women often play out "not enough and abdication of power" and men often play out "arrogance and abuse of power." We can see this in relationships, families, business, teams, and political parties everywhere in the world.

We can even fine tune that further and say the "feminine" and the "masculine" have tended in those directions for many, many, many years now.

The winds are shifting. A quality of Source that is harmony is emerging, which automatically flushes out disharmony. There are messes to clean up as a result. We see this playing out in the world now.

We're literally constantly seeking connection with Source. This seeking registers as an insatiable hunger. Thus, we scour the smorgasbord of life in hopes of finding what we seek.

"Yes, that's how it feels to me, I just didn't know how to describe it!" exclaimed Marta.

I get it! It's miserable to be so hungry, but not be able to feed the hunger.

Here's the first step in reversing heart disease. It is the conscious choice to be called back to Love. To offer the rest of your life to this journey home. To cultivate a union with love as your state of being. To allow her to show you the way, step by step.

It's OK to have no idea what that means or how to do it. It's something we cultivate day in and day out. It builds in momentum. There's no way to do this wrong.

The President of the United States gives a "State of the Union Address" meant to inform Congress and offer recommendations. As we seek union with our own Divinity, it's wise to assess how that's going. Some days, the "State of your Union" with Love is glorious and amazing and you can't imagine it ever being less than this. Other days, the State of your Union seems untouchable and miserable.

When devoted to Love, all states are part of the journey. When learning to play music, almost all the notes are played off key in the beginning. It is with regular practice that we begin playing on key, and harmony is developed. Over time, not overnight.

Here's the thing: there's nowhere else to turn, nowhere else to go but home to Love. When I finally realized that, it made things much simpler. Which doesn't mean it's easy, but it is simple, and it's a lot easier than being miserable in the darkness of solitary confinement (a.k.a. separated from Source).

"I'm in," said Marta. "And I'm a little scared of saying that too."

Totally get it, and that's normal to have a mixture of excitement and fear. You will find that turning to Love is gentle. Resistance is harsh. Love is gentle. She will guide you every breath of the way.

One of my regular invitations to Love is this:

"Divine Love, thank you for gently ordering my mind, body, and life." I say this to myself anytime I think of it throughout the day. First thing in the morning, in the shower, while driving, and most certainly when I feel off key.

So incredibly soothing. For the record, that's just one of many invitations and invocations.

Divine Love Herself will teach you how to trust. She will help you bridge your humanity and your Divinity. That alone is a "thing" and takes the time it takes. We'll definitely talk more about that.

"Does that help a little?" I asked Marta.

"It does, and then my mind gets all spun up in how, and when, and will it work for me, I'm probably more broken than the average person, yada, yada, yada. Do you know what I mean?" she said.

Definitely. Notice that this is exactly what gets us into trouble. We give our mind free reign, usually leave our heart out of the equation, and definitely don't invite Spirit to the party. Results of that equation equals stuck.

For the record: everyone thinks they are the exception to the rule. That "they" are the one who's beyond repair, so broken that it's pointless to even try. Which is a BFL (Big Fat Lie).

A disconnected mind works hard to convince you that you are broken. Which is another flat out lie. Source, of which you and I are an extension of, could never be broken.

It's practice, like training a dog or learning an instrument or building a muscle. There's where you are and where you want to go. That's true for everyone choosing to awaken to wholeness. We start where we are. Success is only guaranteed with Love involved.

There is only one rule: never give up.

Deep down, your heart already knows you are whole. The heart knows the truth of oneness with Love. You've been called to wake up to that, otherwise you and I would be nowhere near this conversation.

To be clear, I'm not saying you don't have a good heart, or that you're not already a good person, I know you're an incredible person with an amazing heart. Otherwise, you wouldn't be getting "the call." Being a good person is a speck compared to the bounty of your whole heart.

I often think, "So what if it takes the rest of my life, what else have I got to do but this? And in fact, everything I 'do' from my ever-developing connection to Love, will be *way* more effective and meaningful than without it."

I will not break the one rule: never give up.

"So, what do I do when my heart starts racing, or when I'm at the doctor's office and feel really scared, or when I can't sleep at night, or when I continue to fail at choosing heart healthy foods? Right now, I feel calm and it all sounds good, but most of the time, I feel overwhelmed." Marta asked with a softness, rare for her.

Sweetie, you practice. You keep showing up for yourself. You let life teach you how. You don't give up. You consciously choose to pivot toward Love. You invite Love to be with you everywhere. You invite her guidance in every decision from which pair of underwear to choose, to which house to buy. The big and the small, she will join you by invitation for everything. Why? Because, she is *all* of it anyway. You trip, fall, and get back up. You find support so you have a better chance of living into your intentions than not. This is how it happens. That's what people do to rise. They get help and support.

Remember, if anyone has done something, it's possible for any other person to do it. You can do this because you're capable, resourceful, and you're free relative to many women in the world. When the Dalai Lama said, "The world will be saved by Western women," he meant it. He meant that western women are relatively free, and while we are still working through "equality issues" in the west, placing our focus there moves the needle far too slowly. Placing our focus on the only force that can truly create change in the world is swift, and is the only option.

You and I are those women. You and I have what it takes to embody Love, to be her open door. Not to save the "whole world," but to influence our own life and any part of the world that happens to intersect our life. That's it, that's our job. That's what you're embarking on as the embodiment of Love, the most powerful influence in the world. You don't have to know anything other than saying yes to Her. We can't get ahead of ourselves, or we'll lose our way.

Here's the thing: there is nothing to lose and everything to gain here.

"This feels like a high-level pep talk," said Marta. "I want to be able to remember it all and I'm a little nervous because since menopause, my mind and memory are, well, let's just say not as spry as they once were. I used to be able to remember everything!"

"You will," I said. "You'll remember exactly what you need, when you need it. How do I know that? Because you have every piece of truth already in your system. As you tend this work consciously, you'll have access to what you need at will and in the right timing."

Here's the thing with menopause. The gathering of years equates to the gathering of tremendous wisdom. That wisdom is like a treasure chest awaiting to be opened. When it all hits the fan at midlife, it's your life and your heart asking for the unfinished business of the first half of life to be healed. It's making room for wisdom to blossom. It's your soul speaking up, no longer staying quiet for the sake of appeasing others. And if your heart isn't connected to what you're doing, who you spend time with, and your highest Self, your heart will take you out of that situation.

When we learn to trust our soul, heart, Source, and Love, we go with the flow rather than resisting change. This is a sacred practice.

It is at this point in life where we consciously decide to become a vessel for Divine Love. If most illness is due to an inhibited Spiritual life (I read that some years ago), then now is the time to get uninhibited.

There are 37.2 trillion cells in your body, and in every single cell there are 37.2 trillion atoms. In every atom is an electron, and that electron is light. It is Divine Intelligence. That's incalculable to the mind, that amount of Life Force that is Love.

We've got to remember, as an "electric" body and heart, every atom has an electron and that electron is Love, it is the surging Life Force of Love. Let's just get out of Her way.

So don't worry that you're "not enough." Rather, decide that you're going to be in a harmonious union with all that Love, which is more than enough. After all, it's right there in your very own body. All that Love is your body, expressing as your body and through your heart.

When we yield to this truth, you can be none other than whole. Heart health is a given because it is not possible for Love herself to be in a state of disease.

That is the true State of Your Union.

Now let's get you on board with it.

Chapter 5: Getting a Grip on Nutrition

"Eat real (whole) food, not too much, mostly plants"
— Michael Pollan

Similar to the intelligence in every cell, there is intelligence in plants. By way of alchemy, digestion, and delivery of nutrients, we are made whole every day by plants.

For as many nutritional opinions as there are out there, almost nobody disagrees with eating real whole food, just not too much, and mostly plants.

What does that mean?

"Real" means food from Mother Earth. "Whole" means the least amount of processing and denaturing by the time it arrives on your plate, including choosing organic to avoid extra toxicity. Real food is a Life Force and it gives you Life Force, but not if there's no Life Force in the food. Real food is alive and processed food is dead. Eating food that is alive gives you life. Eating dead food, over time, gives rise to death.

"Not too much" means no more than your body requires at any given sitting. Otherwise, your body has to overwork to manage the "too much." From midlife forward, we don't have extra energy reserves to manage the excess day in and day out. It would be like stealing from your retirement account to gamble the funds away. Not wise. We were able to get away with it in youth, because reserves were ample.

"Mostly plants" means find your balance. If you eat flesh protein, those protein portions would be modest in comparison to the plants portion.

If you don't eat flesh protein, it's a bit easier. If you're eating whole and real, then your options are already mostly plants.

The research for heart health continues to show that eating an all or mostly plant-based diet greatly supports heart health. In fact, when people shift away from processed, standard American diet fare to mostly plant-based, their heart health markers dramatically improve in as little as three weeks.

You may know all this already. You may even agree. But there's a gap between knowing, agreeing, and living it. I get it.

There is only one way that I know of to line up with and live a heart healthy diet as a lifestyle (happily I might add). The very diet that is a major factor in reversing this fatal disease.

Give it a try for ninety days in partnership with your Higher Wiser Divine Self. This Higher Self or Divine Self is the part of us that is eternally pure and connected to Love. It's often considered to hover above us until we exchange dense energy in our system for that higher light. There is also a Divine Spark in every single heart. Some have fanned the flame of that spark to become more, some have not. The Divinity within your heart eventually connects fully with your Higher Self or Presence as you become more aligned with your True Nature of Love. Partnership with your Higher Self is the only way. How do I know? Because I've been obsessed with nutrition for forty years. I did my master's thesis on nutrition. I've tried every diet out there.

I've gone back and forth between eating sugar and not eating sugar. Between being vegetarian, tending toward Mediterranean, to Paleo, to full-on Keto, and everything in between.

When I was younger, it was always to lose weight. As I gathered my years, it became to feel well and not die prematurely because of metabolic syndrome and heart disease.

I'll share with you what I've learned, what the epic failures taught me, and what definitely moves the needle. And this isn't just my experience. It's the experience of every woman who gets a grip on her nutrition.

Energy, Matter, and You

You are matter, are you not? You can see yourself reflected back in the mirror because you are matter. You are vibrating at a dense enough frequency that the naked eye can see. The same is true of the chair you're sitting on and the home you live in.

Everything, every single thing you see is energy. The same is true for all the spaces in and around, what your eye can see, and the unseen. That's also energy. Matter is that which occupies space at varying degrees of particles and atoms.

In between the seen particles is so much unseen energy, it's staggering. In fact, it is thought that a human being is ninety-six percent unseen energy, which means our actual body is only four percent of our entire being.

When we start to consider that we are biophoton and bio-electric in nature (bio meaning physical biology or matter, photon meaning the light that resides inside every cell, and electric meaning the electron in every atom that holds to blueprint for health), and that there is more empty space than there is stuff in the empty space (just look up and all around to notice that), then it starts to make sense that who we are is more energy and less of the denser, seen matter.

We renew and replenish energy every day with food, liquids, breath, and our choice of thoughts. Each of these elements are a form of Qi in Chinese medicine. Because cells are constantly turning over, nourishing and repairing your body, the quality of the fuel we fill our vessels with daily matters.

A lot.

Qi, by the way, is Life Force. Qi is light and Love. Qi just happens to be the Chinese word for life, light, and Love. Same, same.

Now, consider that the Latin word "*mater*" means mother. Mother Earth supplies the plants from which we nourish our own matter, or what we refer to as our body, day in and day out. Plant intelligence converts to cellular intelligence. The more we deviate from that incredible exchange of Life Force, the more our health deviates from wholeness.

It's one thing to conceptually agree with the what and why of good nutrition, and another thing altogether to master the "how."

- How to get all those plants in amid a busy life?
- How to crave kale over a Krispy Kreme or whatever is your own personal kryptonite?
- How to be inspired by a smoothie?
- How to go out or travel and still stay on track?
- How to not be owned by sugar and cravings?

If you were to look back on the amount of time, energy, and money you've spent on trying to do the right thing nutritionally, for some women, it's a lot. Definitely true for me.

The Superhero in You, Ready to Don Her Cape

Let's use the Marvel supercharacter analogy. I'm not really a Marvel, sci-fi, or fantasy film girl, but I know enough to translate the analogy.

The villain represents the dark against the superhero, who is the light. In the case of food, the villain (literally) is the dark, dead food, and the superhero is the light that is carried in whole, living food. Seriously. Contemplate that until it lands.

The point of being a Spirit-centered woman is to become the light and Love that is our true nature. To exchange old, dead false beliefs, stories, density, and self-perceptions for the light of our True Nature.

By the way, we can't do that without our superhero Self (which is always Source). Why? Because our old habitual patterns will run the show every time without the superhero coming in to save the day.

You, your Higher Self, your soul, your heart, your Spirit, the very energy that is beating your heart right *now is* your superheroine. And superheroines have super-powers. Otherwise, why bother! It's the super-powers that make it fun. Look at Marvel's modern Wonder Woman. She's a boss. It doesn't matter if you saw the movie *Wonder Woman* or don't even like this superhero/power analogy.

Here's what matters: it's an archetype which is a template or a pattern of behavior, a model that we ourselves can merge into.

The Emergence of Masculine/Feminine Balance Is Happening Now

The Divine Feminine is reemerging. It's showing up in movies, art, books, and real life examples of women speaking their truth and daring to be empowered. This is the kind of power that reveres life, rather than destroys it. It's happening, and there is no turning back.

It's happening after a long, arduous spell of patriarchal dominance, apparently having played out for the purpose of exploring power. The exploration went well over the line, but hey, that's just my opinion.

The harmonious balance of the masculine and feminine is the order of the day. Not only in a large scale way on the planet, but in each of us as individuals too.

The Divine Feminine can be seen in the archetype of Divine Mother, which is the ever present "presence" of Divine Love awakening in humanity. This presence is everywhere in the seen and the unseen. We can only behold it as we wake up to it.

Light is the activity that carries Love wherever there is life. If you wish to fill yourself with more light and Love and claim life for yourself (I assert that there is nothing you want more, for it carries every single thing your heart desires), then filling yourself with light and Love becomes your priority.

Digestive Qi and Eating Light

A few pages ago, I mentioned that the wisdom of Chinese medicine teaches us that we fill ourselves with Qi by way of our food, drink, breath, and I always add our thoughts. Thoughts are our most subtle form of Qi.

How to do this?

Eat light. Breathe light. Think light. See light. Remember that Love is always carried by this light. Divine light is a form of nourishment we haven't given much attention to.

What foods carry light? Plants.

How to breathe light? Be present, breathe deep all day, and intend for your breaths to carry the unseen molecules of light that fill the air.

Fill your mind with light. In doing this, it carries Higher Intelligence and teaches your small, fear-based mind to trust what is good and whole.

Research shows that if you "see" yourself eating more whole foods, you will. If you "see" healthy, whole foods in your kitchen, you'll eat more of them. This whole book could be just about our capacity to "see" or "envision" our wholeness into being. Using this force to bring more nourishment into your life is a powerful and worthy practice.

Stand in the produce section of your grocery story and feel the Life Force. It's in the color and sheer quantity. Mostly it's in the food itself. Breathe it in, ask the Life Force of live food to connect with you. Ask the Qi in live food in your kitchen to nourish you at the highest level possible.

Why is this of great importance?

Beside the fact that it's who you really are, you can't strong-arm yourself into heart healthy nutrition because it doesn't last, ends up causing rebellion, and increases resistance. Nothing good there.

When you start with the roots of your True Nature, not only do you tap into unfailing success, over time, you *become* your True Nature. You become a being of light and Love. You are nourished by life, which pivots all your energy away from premature death.

This is the thing every woman is seeking. We look for it in odd external places, don't we? The Holy Grail is inside you. It's the light that is you. It *is* you. The you that is aligned with your True Nature.

The quality of health, wholeness, longevity, and happiness is in direct proportion to the quality of connection to your Divinity. Divinity is the same thing as Source, Spirit, heart, consciousness, Love, Qi, God, The Universe, Creative Life Force, or light.

Yin and Yang, another concept in Chinese medicine, is represented by our bodies. All things material such as blood, lymph, tears, synovial fluid, tissue etc. is Yin. All things unseen such as warmth, movement, circulation, activity, and function is Yang.

Yin is matter. Yang is (unseen) activity, like the wind causing movement, and while we don't see the wind, we certainly can't say the wind and the movement it causes doesn't exist. We don't "see" our thoughts, but they, and their cause, certainly exist.

Yin is feminine. Yang is masculine. Balance between the two is health.

Yin is Love. Yang is light. Balance between the two is the harmonious flow of life.

Honor both, for they are inseparable. They are the One.

Speaking of activity and function, let me give you an important visual for food, nourishment, and Life Force.

We have a finite amount of digestive Qi at any given time. Imagine a four-cup measuring beaker, half filled. So, there are two cups of digestive Qi available in the measuring cup. Then you eat four cups of food in your meal, yet you only have two cups of digestive Qi to receive the food, break it all down, extract the nutrients, dispose of the waste, while at the same time sending the nutrients into the blood stream to be carried to all parts of the body for renewal, reparation, and creating energy.

That's a lot going on, right?

Two cups digestive Qi, four cups food to break down. Being two cups short is the problem. It's a burden to the body. We can get away with it every once in a while, but not every day and in every meal, which honestly, is the way most of us do it. Remember the part "not too much" in the opening quote?

To add the burden, we eat food that is hard to break down. Plants are easier to break down because they carry their own digestive enzymes with them. These enzymes act as assistants to the digestive Qi and help to break the food down. Dead food not only doesn't have that, it costs the body a lot to figure out what it is, where the nutrients are, and how to get it transported. A Krispy Kreme (or your own personal kryptonite) often gets stored as fat because there's not much value to the body in terms of nourishment.

Our body is so smart. She stores toxins and junk in fat to keep as much gunk as possible away from important organ function and bodily happenings as protection. I'm totally fist bumping my body right now. Feel free to partake if you're feeling it too.

There was a point some years ago where I was literally doing everything right in terms of food, exercise, sleep, meditating. People, including myself, would say they didn't know anyone who was more devoted to all the parts as I was.

Yet, my health and energy still felt like it was struggling. I was so frustrated, and I often blurted out loud, "What else am I supposed to be doing here?!" Sometimes there were a few expletives, you can use your imagination. That went on for longer than I care to admit until one day, as I'd done so many times in the past, I put my hand on my heart and asked her what I was missing.

That's called surrender. With surrender always comes guidance. I was guided to begin the work of filling my mind, body, and life with light. The light of colors, breathing light into my body with every breath I could remember to be present to, asking the food I "thought" my body needed if it would contribute to my light body or not, and in what amounts. I began choosing foods that made me light. I envision waterfalls of light pouring through the top of my head filling my mind, heart, body, and life with light. I envision the light in every cell bursting forth.

Game changer. Everything upshifted at this point, and there's been no turning back. I crave the light in these ways now. I would go so far as to say that this light and Love is what I was hungry for, not for the kryptonite that seems like the only food that will feed the empty hunger.

As a human being, emptiness can only be filled with our own Divinity. When we yield to this Divinity, she teaches us good choices, and helps us make those choices become easy.

Without connection to Divinity, those choices are hard or impossible.

With connection to your Divinity, those choices become normal and natural.

At first, I couldn't see the light. Now it's as normal as the nose on my face. I persisted because I was desperate. We do that as humans when we've seemingly exhausted all the options, we do the things we most likely would have rolled our eyes at a year ago. And when they work, it's awe inspiring.

Feeding Your Starving Cells

My cells, your cells, are craving concentrated, light-filled nutrition because that concentrated nutrition is deep cellular nutrition. Regular deep cellular nutrition virtually eliminates physical cravings. A healthy body must have that, especially in the second half of life. It's one of the reasons I like smoothies, because I don't know many people who can eat the piles of greens the body needs to repair and renew. I had a woman tell me just the other day, "I don't have time for those piles, and besides, all that chewing is exhausting!"

But I can shove those same piles into a NutriBullet with some yummy fruit and some other flavorful concentrated nutrition, and I literally feel the nutrition and light sparking awake within a few moments. Every time. Seriously.

I like the NutriBullet 900 (I have no vested interest in sharing this brand with you other than it works), because it masticates the food for you, maximally breaking it down for that deep cellular nutrition to be bioavailable, which means it can get into the cells where it needs to be without sacrificing any of the nutrients. Almost one hundred percent of the nutrients are left intact. Remember our two cups of digestive Qi? With a smoothie, we don't have to spend any Qi to break the food down. We don't even have to chew ... huge energy saver according to the woman who said it would be too exhausting to eat all those greens.

You can carry a smoothie with you to work or to run errands, eating when your body is ready, not just when there's a time slot for eating.

Deeper nutrition also means that some supplements are important. There are very specific supplements that support heart health. Below is a basic foundational list from which you can build upon:

- Co-enzyme Q 10
- Magnesium
- EFAs/omegas (especially if you don't eat fish)
- Vit D3
- MSM (because of how important sulfur is to heart health)

This is not an exhaustive list by any means, but it's a start. It's also important that you're getting enough fiber. I'm a big fan of prebiotics, probiotics, and a good multi-vitamin/mineral supplement.

A client from some years ago, who is currently enjoying her healthy, Love-filled life at eighty-six, said to me one day, "I don't like taking stuff, I don't want my kitchen counter filled with supplement bottles, I have a small basket and everything I'm willing to take must fit in that basket or I'm not doing it!" She made a circle with her hands about how big the basket was, and it was small.

I said, "Dina, we weren't really designed to live much past child rearing ages, so if you want to be healthy as you age, you've got to give your body what it needs to function well. And the argument that we can get it all in our food is not sound. There are too many variables that have changed in the twenty-first century. Our soils are not as rich in nutrients as they were fifty years ago. There are more toxins in the air, water, and food supply that bombard our system that weren't around years ago. Our stress levels burn through nutrients like a wildfire burns through brush. You've got to be willing to supplement. Personally, I think of supplements as a form of food and I wouldn't think of depriving myself of food!"

Honestly, the argument for "too many supplements" for someone who wants to build better than average health just doesn't hold water. In my mind, to create health, I've just got to let that go and give my body what it needs. The resistance to supplements is not only a waste of my energy, but it robs me of a higher level of health.

I steward a similar argument when it comes to sleep. Cheating yourself of sleep is a major faux pas and here's why. In Chinese medicine, we have a tank of Qi, full when we're born, so to speak, and we die when it is empty. How we nourish our Qi from birth to death determines our health. This battery pack or tank of Qi is held within the kidney/adrenal energy system, according to the Chinese medical model. This system replenishes with sleep, especially the sleep it gets before midnight. Burning the candle at both ends and cheating yourself of sleep siphons your tank. It's costly.

Digestion and adrenal health are closely linked.

And here's an even bigger clincher…. Your digestive energy system is just below your heart center. Thus, digestive health acts as a foundation or substructure to your heart health. A strong digestive center supports your heart. Weak digestive function, on the other hand, can't support your heart in the manner she requires.

Here's literally how I see this now. I'm devoted to Love because anything less than that is miserable. Thus, I eat for Love. I choose based on how well it supports Love. Just this one piece alone does more to contribute to the healing of the world than any non-profit, for profit, volunteer or charity work one could do every moment of their waking life, for the rest of their life.

Why?

Because most people are doing those things from an empty-of-their-Divinity place, which doesn't offer, or extend from every cell in their body, the only energy on the planet that heals, which is Love.

While it's noble to engage in work that saves the world, it's a hamster wheel unless it carries the energy of Love with it. Only Love can change the old energy, the false beliefs, the ills of the world. Love needs a body, and you're it. I'm it. Go tag someone else, please.

I wrote this in 2016 and it's quite applicable here: "When a wise person talks about replacing fear with Love, an ordinary person is apt to dismiss the idea as impossible, lofty, and pious. But the fact is, the wise person is telling you something, which is one of the first laws of hygiene as well as ethics. No person, even for the body's, sake can afford to indulge in fear. It is akin to repeated doses of poison. When you are urged to return fear to love, you are not listening to a moon-struck idealist; rather you are hearing counsel that is as significant to health as advice about diet. This process has nothing to do with anything on the outside; it's an inside job. The outside trigger serves to show us the fear that is ready to be Loved free. As the mind rebels, and the heart rejoices, do it anyway. It's the point of life."

Here are some of the ways I've learned to "weave this into everyday life."

- Start with one meal at a time and clean it up. Figure out the various options you'd like to choose from. Take however long you need to get a groove with that meal and when it feels like you've got into your groove, move on to the next meal and do the same.

- Prepare ahead of time. I don't even know how it's possible to eat healthy without preparing ahead. Have the foods and ingredients you need available. Prepare dishes you can eat over the week. Freeze extra portions for later, especially when in a pinch.

    1. Part of preparation is knowing where you're going when you go out to eat and/or travel. You'll have to do some looking up of what you'll have available to you so you can fill in the gaps. If you don't know the restaurant, then be the one who makes a suggestion for one you already know is healthy and works well.

    2. Bring food and snacks with you on the go. Tuck them into your purse and don't make a big deal of it, just nonchalantly take care of yourself.

    3. Like taking supplements, you have to get over the fact that there's preparation involved. I've turned that preparation into a meditation and a time to connect with the Life Force in the food, connecting with and sending gratitude to Mother Earth for providing it. Prep time is sacred time to me now which feels different than a chore.

- *Decide what you'll do for your regular meals* "in a pinch," have those options available because life happens. What's your plan B?

- *Create and follow a plan.* You'll be successful when you're clear about why this is "your" plan and what it will do for you.

- *Eat when you're hungry,* and if you're not physiologically hungry, wait until you are. That digestive Qi we talked about needs time to refill. Eating before the body is ready, before there's enough digestive Qi, means we eat when the cup has only half to one cup of digestive Qi to four cups of food. Makes it even harder on the body.

If you're not aware of the different feelings of hunger, take a little time to learn those in your own body. A normal and real hunger arises slowly and there's no desperation to eat, just the awareness that you're going to want to eat at some point in the next hour or so. Even then, sometimes that passes.

An immediate, "I've got to eat now, and I've got to eat this thing to make this empty feeling go away" is usually emotional and not true physiological hunger. You've been around long enough to know that feeding emotions is a bottomless pit that leaves you feeling miserable and mad at yourself.

- *Make a list of things you can do instead of eating* when that emptiness is all consuming. We'll talk about some cool things in Chapter 10 on this note.

If you're worried about where you'll find the time to do these extra things, there's a whole chapter on time coming up.

- *Use your capacity to envision* yourself ahead of time preparing healthy food, going to bed at a time you know serves you best, seeing your light showers, etc.

Every time I'm resistant and rebellious about doing something I know I "should" and really want to do, but can't seem to get there, I stop putting pressure on myself to do it, and instead just see myself doing it.

Then within a couple of days, I'm actually doing it. I kid you not, this works every time.

See yourself doing the thing, and eventually your system steps right into it. I said earlier to give yourself time, that it's not a switch we flip for overnight success. I'll amend that now and say that when you use your capacity to envision and see yourself doing the thing, time will collapse in your favor, and you'll have access to that thing in real time sooner rather than later. We'll talk more about this in the chapter on time. It's exciting research on our human potential.

- I find it helpful to have absolute *clarity about what's off limits*. To me, I feel like I can be free when held within a structure. So, it's not about rigidity as much as it is about being held. Below is a list of what is not inside my corral of free choice. Inside my corral of free choice are whole, real, alive plants prepared deliciously to my taste. Outside the corral are things like:
  - GMOs
  - Vegetable oils, especially Canola Oil
  - Soy products
  - Gluten (if you're sensitive, which I am)
  - Refined sugar, especially if it's non-organic

Personally, I don't eat corn, dairy, eggs, or meat, just my choice because I feel really good as a result.

Inside my corral are all the colorful plants, fruits, vegetables, legumes I can dream up. Something really interesting happened when I embarked on this plant-based journey a few years back after being *all* about low-carb, paleo, and keto for at least a dozen years. I noticed that, for no reason, I felt happy and serene.

When I was eating animal products, I'd wake up in the middle of the night with irrational fear that I couldn't find my way through. I'd read, coincidentally, in several spiritual books in a span of a few months, that you can't cook the vibration of fear out of animal foods. That resonated instantly, and I thought I'd give it a try for ninety days. After ninety days, I felt so good, the irrational fear at night stopped, I slept better, and felt light and happy, so I just kept going with it. That's the feeling I'd been asking for several years, but couldn't access it in the density of how much animal and fat foods I'd been eating.

We each have to find our own balance with this. I'm not saying I think you should do what I did, I'm saying you should explore and find the best balance for your body. That's all we can do, really.

As you start with that simple suggestion from the beginning of this chapter, "Eat real food, not too much, and mostly plants," connect to the wisdom of your Divinity, and you'll find your best balance, because that's the only way it works.

Nutrition is a dynamic dance. It's not a static position. It's all about finding your right rhythm.

Other Important Mouth Activities

Other important considerations in heart health involving what happens in our mouth are:

- Not smoking, or quitting if you already do.
- Drinking enough clean water. Since our body is about two-thirds water, you can also intend that the water you drink carry messages of healing throughout your body. If you're not familiar with the book *The Hidden Messages in Water* by scientist Masaru Emoto, it's fascinating material. His research shows that the molecules of water change based on our intentions and thoughts. They become crystalline-like with healthy messages and deranged with negative messages.

71

- Low-to-no alcohol. If you choose low (which I do), as a woman, that means no more than one drink at a time and no more than three times per week. I prefer red wine for its benefits.
- Taking care of your teeth and gums, since oral health and heart health share a strong link. Holistic dentistry is the next evolution of the dental field and holistic dentists approach oral health from the perspective of whole-body health.

A mouthful here, I realize! Taking it one step, one bite at a time gets you there. Over time, when you add all this up, your cells become lighter and more nourished. Nourished cells not only heal, but also give you a higher level of energy. Shall we take that energy and go dancing?

Chapter 6: Would You Like to Dance?

"Dance is the hidden language of the soul of the body. Great dancers are not great because of their technique, they are great because of their passion. Movement never lies. It is a barometer telling the state of the soul's weather to all who can read it."

— Martha Graham

So far, we've talked about the first two steps to reversing heart disease. Step one is the conscious connection to Source with the intention of cultivating love in every particle of our being and pocket of our life.

Step two was the nourishment of our body with whole foods that contain the very light that sustains a healthy heart and body.

Step three is all about our dance with life. Literally, with dance representing movement.

Let's talk about working out.

First of all, after working for decades now, who wants to squeeze in more "work" before or after work?

Who wants to push through something that doesn't feel good?

Something to know about Love. She wants every choice to feel nourishing. To add energy, not suck energy.

As a Spirit currently being expressed in a body, movement is vital. Why? Because movement is life.

Life doesn't stop flowing. Even after death, life still flows. It may change form, but it doesn't stop.

The former director of NASA's Life Sciences Division, Joan Vernikos, Ph.D. published a book back in 2011 called *Sitting Kills, Moving Heals*. An inconspicuous little book that packs a powerful punch.

She studied astronauts for decades and learned that when a human body is outside of gravity, as astronauts are, the return to gravity is accompanied by several health challenges. Muscle wasting, bone loss, decreased blood volume, increased body fat, achy joints, a depressed immune system, loss of collagen, decreased cardiac output, reduced insulin sensitivity (that's bad, we want optimal insulin sensitivity for stable blood sugar and cellular energy production), and sluggish gut, to name a few.

There's the plot twist to her research. She found that regular (non-astronaut) people have the very same health challenges because they sit too much. She talks about how, before the invention of washing machines and garage door openers, we moved much more than we do today. She refers to this type of movement that should be happening all day as "non-exercise activity."

The problem is we don't do nearly enough of that type of movement. We are meant to be perpetual movement machines – otherwise gravity takes over and we're subject to the same problems as an astronaut. It's important because muscle fibers respond to non-exercise or natural physical activities distributed intermittently throughout the day.

"Working out" for an hour three times a week offers a different kind of muscle/body response. But it's the non-exercise activity that is a much greater component of your body's total energy than structured workouts.

"What?!" you might say, "But I thought working out was a good thing?"

And I would say regular movement is a good thing and working out is better than nothing, but if that three times a week workout schedule is deluding you into thinking, "I'm good," well then, it's just what it is ... a delusion. Sorry to be harsh about it, but it's really, really important for you to understand.

Movement throughout the day, such as the small, brief, yet frequent muscular movements one makes throughout the day, are vital. Those where you are changing position are the most effective: standing, sitting, lying down, bending (to pick something up), squatting, stretching, (reaching) upward, playing an instrument, or fidgeting in general.

Sitting at a desk, as many do all day, does not engage nearly enough of this type of movement. And the consequences of that are deadly.

Too little movement or too much sitting leads to what has become known as "lipotoxicity," or the accumulation of abnormal metabolites such as triglycerides and other end products that stiffen the heart and blood vessels.

All of this is the reason standing work-stations have become more popular in the last decade or so. Simply standing involves much more movement than sitting.

There are many intricacies to the distinction between non-physical activity (little movements throughout the day) and higher intensity exercises such as running, walking, cycling, or working out in a gym.

One example is that bone responds to signals that are "more like buzzing than pounding."

I am *not* saying to ditch your daily walk. Not at all. I am saying that a daily walk or workout isn't a substitute for what movement throughout the day does for a human body. We need both.

That's our design.

You might know someone who is relentless with her workout regime. She does a high-intensity something every day, and it's usually long. I know a woman who walks several hours a day and has for years, yet her bone density is failing. Some would say that it's because her mom had osteoporosis, but I bet if the balance between her non-exercise activity and her workout routine were analyzed, she would be in excess with her workouts, and too low, or deficient, in her non-exercise or natural physical activities distributed intermittently throughout the day. As most of us are unless we become conscious and do something about it.

Dr. Vernikos refers to our need for "gravity-habits." She suggests developing the "G-habit" of standing up often. Changing our position relative to gravity is the most beneficial way of using gravity. Research shows that a level change is needed every fifteen minutes to avoid the effects of gravity.

This is a perfect example of "getting out of the way," so the body can do what she's designed to do – be whole.

Otherwise, gravity uses us. And it's very seductive. The lure of gravity can pull us down into a comfy chair and have us not move for hours.

At the end of this chapter, we'll talk about ideas for movement, but before we do, I want to offer another perspective for you to consider.

Movement activates light in cells, which releases density. In order to hold your own light, you require a body that moves. Otherwise you'll feel incapable of returning density for light (our design) because you'll feel wiped out, overwhelmed, and overpowered.

The fatigue from lack of movement becomes its own catch-22. You don't have the energy to move, but it's movement that gives you energy.

Start small. And start with movement you enjoy. It's the only way I've found to keep it up over time. If you find it hard to "fit in regular workouts," or if you're on track for a while, then you veer off the rails – first of all, you're not alone. Second of all, it may be the non-physical activity your body is craving.

Listening to Your Body at Least as Much (Preferably More) Than Your Head

We've not been taught to listen to our body, let alone honor her by giving her a version of movement that is joyful. For some women, just *being* and staying in her body is a feat. Showing up like this regularly is a discipline that shows your entire system that you are willing to build strength for the embodiment of Divine Love.

Embodying light and Love and supporting the ways for it to pour forth from every cell is the point of being in a body. We become conscious of being Spirit-centered as a mental awareness first, in order to embody it fully.

It feels good to move in ways your body asks for. To me, that is the opposite of "pushing through a workout," because it's what we think we're supposed to do. I no longer "push;" rather, I inspire myself by remembering how good I feel when I move. I do what I can with the energy levels I have to work with, rather than blowing off movement altogether. During my more rebellious moments, I say, "Let's just start with this tiny small step, and if we don't like it, we can stop." I'll tell you that ninety-eight percent of the time, I just keep moving rather than stopping. No pressure, just a little nudge.

If a hard workout feels good, then do it. I like that too sometimes, but what I really love is dancing, stretching, walking amid beauty, turning compost, and moving all day rather than sitting. Maybe you like playing a sport?

Don't get me wrong, I sit and rest when my body needs it, but it's not my habit to sit for hours every day. In fact, once I get up in the morning, it could be five or six hours before my butt hits a seat. I just don't understand how someone can get up after lying in bed for seven or eight hours, then sit down to drink coffee or tea, or whatever else they do sitting down!

My bottom would feel so squished and compressed! That feeling when your derriere feels as smashed as a ball of wadded up foil from sitting too long. I learned this about myself years ago, and even try to book airline flights that aren't too early so I have time to move before having to sit for the flight.

I'm standing right now, typing this love letter to you, but the first couple of chapters I sat, and I paid the price. My sacrum got jammed up into my lower back, and my right hip joint felt squeezed by all those compressed butt muscles. It was aching at night, and it was only after several days, lots of stretching, and changing my writing position that it eased up.

You may know that back pain is a huge problem affecting at least eighty percent of the population at one time or another. As we've just learned, heart health is affected by too little movement, and I don't think it's any coincidence that both problems have arisen in proportion to the increased amount of sitting over the past decades. Knowing what we know about gravity and the effects on a human body, it makes sense.

Since every cell of our body is made from light and Love (don't worry if you still can't wrap your mind around that), then moving in ways you love is harmonious, while moving in ways you don't love but think you "should" be doing is disharmonious. And disharmony has consequences over time.

Let's talk about movement options.

In her book, Dr. Vernikos says that the key to success lies in increasing the amount of natural, habitual physical activity throughout the day. Other researchers have come to the same conclusions: the Russians in working with their cosmonauts, and many other reputable researchers from USC, Berkley, University of Missouri, New York State University, and others have all reached the same results.

For optimal effectiveness, the intensity of your G-habits should be gentle movements that challenge gravity's direction. Tai Chi is a good example of this and is rooted in ancient wisdom.

If you sit a lot, cultivate the habit of simply standing up every twenty minutes. The level change alone makes a difference and is the single most important habit you can cultivate. You don't even have to pace your office, just stand up, reach for the ceiling, take some deep breaths, clear your mind, and return to what you were doing. Then sometimes, do this movement very slowly.

What Dr. Vernikos says about this habit is that it's the key to independence as we age. It helps with blood pressure control and benefits muscles, joints, bones, and balance.

Other movements such as vacuuming, raking, gardening, carrying something heavy (like grocery bags), cracking nuts or juicing lemons by hand, washing a wall or scrubbing a tub are useful as well. You can vary the speed of these movements just like an intermittent workout, alternating between fast and slow.

I've got to say something about stretching. I've been stretching daily since I was sixteen. It started with dancing and never stopped. The dance stopped for thirty-five years, but it's back in my life now because it's so fun.

Some years ago, I said to the Divine, "OK, this body is made up of all your particles and my small mind is clueless about what to feed it, how to move it, and what feels good. I give you full command over this body. Show me what it needs, wants, and likes."

Moving to music is one of the things She asked for, and She was right. Initially, I just put music on and moved. Then I found a dance class with the coolest teacher and other women my age. We rock it. The teacher will say things like, "If your body doesn't move this way anymore, then just do what you can." She gets it.

Back to stretching – there is no other movement we can do that stretches a muscle open. Not even sleeping gives us this. It's important because every little movement we make has cellular byproduct of waste. It's stretching and movement that flushes that waste out of our body. Otherwise, it hangs out as a toxic cesspool with nowhere to go. Every single muscle is made up of thousands of muscle fibers, and when the muscles aren't stretched, those fibers curl up, which traps the waste inside rather than releasing it.

A simple stretch routine, five to ten minutes a day, stretching open all your major muscles from head to toe, opens the flow. What I've noticed is that, once a muscle is stretched and opened, there's a spark of light that's activated, and it feels so good. Seriously, how good it feels is my motivation to do it daily.

It also reduces muscle tension, increases range of motion, opens the joints, improves coordination, and increases blood circulation throughout body, which in turn increases energy levels. It also relieves stress and tightens the skin.

Other ways of consciously improving your movement:

- Stand up straight, and walk tall too.
- Stretch during the day when you have a spare ten seconds, such as by opening up your front chest (pectoral) muscles and holding on to a door jamb for a few breaths as you walk through. Stretch your neck while waiting for your tea water.
- Take the stairs. Park further away instead of close to your destination.
- Put your pants, socks, and shoes on while balancing on the other leg rather than sitting or leaning to hold yourself up. This is great for balance and builds ab strength. You'll get better at it over

time. This helps with balance so we don't fall as we age.
- Sweep by hand, like in the old days. Not that you use this, but don't get me started on those leaf blowers.
- Play ping pong, jump rope, go for a swim, or kayak.

For movement that involves what we think of as "working out," consider a variety such as:
- Tai Chi (considered to be like a moving meditation with excellent benefits)
- Yoga
- Walk daily (I like walking where there is beauty)
- Take a dance class or just put on your favorite music and move
- Swimming
- Mini-trampoline
- Bicycle (stationary or street)
- High Intensity Interval Training (HIIT)
- Rowing machine
- Bodyweight or strengthening exercises
- Anything else you love that feels more like fun than pressure
- No matter what you do, remember to breathe

If movement has been a sore spot for you during your life, then I suggest *seeing* yourself moving in your mind's eye. Imagine yourself moving and enjoying how your body feels while doing it. Envision having the time for movement. Always celebrate yourself when you move and appreciate how you feel, because that makes it easier to continue. Energy follows our awareness, so when we see, celebrate, and appreciate ourselves for doing something, we'll continue to cause and create more of that.

Doing different movements that you find fun is the key. Or at the very least, you'll feel better for having done it. Mix it up over the week. Give yourself permission to play with all this, invite Love, and watch how creative her ideas and inspirations are. Experiment without judgment so you can find your personal sweet spots. It'll pay off in more ways than we can articulate on these pages.

One of the "tricks" I've learned over the years is to just take the first step. Even though I don't "want" to work out half the time, I focus on how good it always feels to get my circulation going and how it puts me in a better mood, not to mention all the health benefits. I'll tell myself, "Just put your workout clothes on and see how you feel." All the while, I'm imagining myself moving. Then I always carry through. I do the same thing with preparing food. I'll just set the bowl out, which makes me feel like the first step is already done, so I might as well keep going forward. I'm always happier for it, and it leaves little room for guilt trips too!

You'll want to take note of your barriers to entry. For example, if I had to drive to a gym, I'd never work out. The extra step of getting in the car, driving over, putting all my stuff in a locker etc., would take me out. All the time. I know this about myself, so I have what I need at home: simple weights, a stationary bicycle. I take walks from my home, too. I need to know I can slide right into my movement, git her done, and move along. No wasted time. But, that's me. You might need the gym to get away from distractions at home that would prevent you from moving. We all find our right recipe.

If you don't give up, I promise you'll find ways to weave joyful movement into your world, all the while replacing guilt with feeling good.

Chapter 7: Cohesion in the Mind

"Calm mind brings inner strength and self-confidence, so that's very important for good health."

— Dalai Lama

Every organ in the body has the ability to regenerate. Even necrotic or dead tissue in the heart can fully regenerate. This is the inside job we've been talking about, the one that's in tandem with your Divinity. There's no other way. It is the Life Force of Love that heals, and that can only be accessed from inside our heart and cells.

Maybe you've heard of neuroplasticity, which is the ability of the brain to form and reorganize synaptic connections and neurons, especially in response to learning or a new experience or following injury. Not only can we make new brain tracks, we can create new communication systems within the brain and body.

There are also about 40,000 specialized neurons in a human heart. Scientists call this the "brain of the heart." The harmony between the heart and the brain is a big deal, which we'll talk about soon.

The point is, we are highly dynamic beings and not as static as we seem. There are often mental constructs that slow our Life Force down so that it seems like nothing really changes. A mental construct is a closely held belief that is not true from the perspective of our highest nature. It's a false belief, not a truth. For example, a false belief is that cells or organs can't regenerate. The truth is that they actually can.

We need cohesion in our brain and mind to move from a static feeling state to a dynamic one.

Let's talk about why that matters and how to consciously create cohesion in your mind.

Have you ever tried to make a positive change in your life? For most of us, in the beginning, our excitement carries us for the first part of the new behavior, but when the initial excitement wears off, we're right back into the old pattern or habit. *So* frustrating!

The lower human mind is to blame here. She doesn't like change. Her job is to protect you, and if you're alive today, then everything you've done up until now is considered safe. According to her, anything new is not safe, and therefore she'll put the brakes on, cause resistance, and talk you out of it (she's really good at that). If you're the tenacious type and subscribe to the "if at first you don't succeed, try again" school, and you're on your umpteenth try, the lower mind will give you a little leeway and make it seem like you're gaining some ground, maybe even let you get close to the finish line. But, more often than not, she'll sneak sabotage right in when you're not looking. Back you go to square one.

Simply put, those who get over the finish line are those who keep moving forward despite setbacks, long enough to create a new brain track for the new behavior, while at the same time taking Life Force away from the old brain track or pattern.

Think of an old country road. Let's say it's the road you walk from home to work every day, and have been for years. It's well worn. Then, someone points out a better path, and you give it a try and realize it is, in fact, a better path. It's not nearly as cleared away and worn as your old path, but you choose it every day anyway because it's shorter, shadier, and more beautiful. Over time, the new path is completely cleared and perfectly suited for your daily walk back and forth from home. What's more, brush begins growing over your old path until you can hardly see it anymore. It's still there. You could still take that path, in fact sometimes, due to nostalgia, you can feel it beckoning you. Nonetheless, you choose your new path because it serves you better.

A very similar thing happens in your brain, which is why we need to talk about the mind and brain for your highest healing.

Your Brain on the Defense

There is a phenomenon in the brain called the defensive mode network. In the whole brain, it operates like a bossy traffic cop, constantly deciding which narratives from the past to reference. This bossy aspect is part of our ego-based small mind and is very much self (with a small "s") referential with a prime directive of safety. She's constantly interpreting what's happening by asking, "What does this mean to me or about me?" It writes and enforces our destructive narratives and tends toward excessive rigidity regarding these damaging stories we tell ourselves. It's the go-to default mode.

On a spectrum of rigidity, states like anxiety, depression, and addiction indicate greater rigidity. All in all, different symptoms may show up from excessive rigidity. This means some people might struggle with depression, while others may have trouble controlling their anxiety, yet another feels doomed by addictive tendencies. Different expressions that all come from the same mental rigidity of the defensive mode network.

Imagine yourself in a room with a twenty-foot high wall (the wall represents the "defensive mode network" in a human mind) that divides the room, leaving about two feet between the ceiling and top of the wall. The left side of the wall is your small mind, which is where you are. On the other side of the wall is your higher intelligence that has access to all your deep desires and potential. If you could get over that wall, you'd be free to live as you desire. But you can't scale the wall. You take running leaps, stack a few chairs to try and get higher, you try everything, but can't quite get yourself over. Thus, you do your best to make a nice life on your side, and you do make a nice enough life given what you've got to work with, but there's a constant tug, some days stronger than others, to try and get over to freedom.

Here's the best news: there are ways to soften and lower the wall. So rather than breaking your body trying to get over the wall, you use your energy to soften and lower the wall, then to simply step over it. Doing that long enough leaves the wall in the lowered position, which makes for cohesion in the mind. This is possible because of neuroplasticity. In and around explanations (food for the mind), the next steps of our journey will be about the *how* to do this! It's very exciting.

Cosmic Field

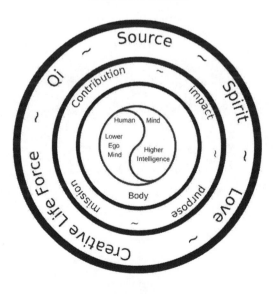

Earth

I wouldn't know how to describe this to you without a visual. So back and forth, we'll reference the circle graphic to learn how this plays out in a human mind, including mine and yours. The lower human ego mind drives the bus until we consciously choose otherwise. This lower human ego part of our mind is like a warden and, like it or not, you and I are the prisoner. The same is true for every human until each one of us lets ourselves out of prison.

The center circle is divided into a left and right side. The left side is our small human mind. For the record, there's nothing wrong with this part of our mind, it's good to be safe. It's not good to be imprisoned. Our goal is to throw you the keys to let yourself out.

We'll call the dividing line or wall the defensive mode network. Living and operating solely from the small mind's point of view is extremely limiting and gives little to no access to wholeness. She is cut off from higher intelligence, represented on the right side of the "wall," as well as being cut off from everything in the other circles in our graphic.

The lower mind has become masterful at hijacking everything, thus it's important to know how she rolls so you can begin making different decisions that favor cohesion in your mind and integration between that small mind part of you and everything else that you are.

When you become conscious of your narratives, stories, and false beliefs, you can release them in favor of what is actually true about all of you. Releasing liberates your Life Force to re-emerge with more of the Love that you are, which is also your power to heal.

The part about this that is not your fault is that these narratives are cultural, religious, passed down through families, lineage, and even DNA programs that make it seem impossible to liberate ourselves. It's not impossible once you recognize the antics and choose differently.

Here are ways to recognize a lower ego mind at work. It:

- Operates in a state of "separation from Source," constantly attempting to control and prove itself (the small mind) as worthy, enough, and OK. It is the primary human wound.
- Is mostly fear-based.
- Creates protective mechanisms of safety.
- Lives from the destructive narrative and false belief that they are imperfect, unworthy, and that Divinity has failed them. It therefore is skeptical and doesn't fully trust Divine Love.
- Tends to be serious about the above points.
- Does *not* want anything to change.
- Is hyper-critical and judgmental of self and others, and often feels like a fraud.
- Has little access to forgiveness due to the core (unconscious) belief that their separation is unforgivable, forever more, and deserves to suffer or be punished.
- Operates from a narrow point of view (POV) and within a closed system.
- Is competitive rather than collaborative.
- Co-opts and hijacks the higher mind (competes with the higher mind rather than collaborates with her).
- Tends to worry, be doubtful, and feel tense, anxious, depressed, and defensive. It fears loneliness and isolation.
- Often feels impatient and burnt out, like a victim, disappointed, even devastated.
- Secretly believes that both itself and the world is broken beyond repair.
- Balks at and may even avoid being a beginner or trying new things.
- Lives in duality (e.g. good/bad, victim/villain, plenty/not enough).

- Constantly sends you on a wild goose chase for remedies and solutions outside of yourself. Grasping is her game.

This last one is interesting because the outer world is so distracting that it leaves little time to go inside. When we build the muscle for going inside, then, and only then, do we connect with the best and highest serving remedies and solutions in the outer world.

The outer world, and the lower mind's obsession with it, can be so loud that she co-opts and dominates the higher mind, which makes change very difficult. There is great wisdom in becoming conscious of the dominate tendencies your lower mind has adopted as her way of hijacking your wholeness. Write them down so your heart can correct the errors. There is always, always, a truth opposite an error.

Your heart and your higher intelligence have access to Source or Spirit or Love because that's the entire field and it flows freely back and forth in a constant dynamic exchange with our higher mind and heart. That connection informs our purpose and impact in our life, as well as our body and its capacity for perfect function, ongoing regeneration, and renewal.

The goal is to create a union or cohesion between the whole mind, left, right, up, down (connecting naturally to the heart), and all around. Whereas the small mind sees duality, the higher heart mind sees oneness. This elevates our consciousness and gives us the best chance we have of leaving behind old, worn, no-longer-good-for-us (in some cases destructive) pathways or brain tracks in favor of a new pathway or brain track that activates the blueprint and intelligence in every cell for wholeness.

Your Inborn Urge to HEAL

Wholeness means Health, Expression or Ease, Abundance, and Love, forming the acronym HEAL. HEALing is available to any human being who chooses it. This is our true nature and potential.

Potential means that it exists in every atom of life awaiting individual activation.

This is the number one purpose, or prime directive, for a conscious, spirit-centered human being – to live as an integrated self. This is curated from the inside out, not from the outside in.

In order to do this, we have to cultivate an awareness of, a relationship with, and compassion for the destructive narratives and stories that hijack our prime directive. As well, you must *become aware of what is really true about your mind, heart, wholeness, and connection to life.*

This is a version of alchemy where you literally compost the old in order to blossom anew. It works. Just wait until you get to Chapter 10.

You'll move from a contracted state of operating in a closed system, to a liberated and open state of being, operating within the intelligence of the Creative Life Force. Wholeness can only be cultivated within the open system and connected to the Creative Life Force.

I have regular touchstones and visuals that remind me to open myself into the benevolent field of wisdom, creative intelligence, and consciousness. In doing so, I contract into the small mind less and less. I live more and more from a state of wholeness rather than the hamster wheel of broken and *not* enough, which is exhausting.

As Henry Cloud put it, "We change our behavior when the pain of staying the same becomes greater than the pain of changing. Consequences give us the pain that motivate us to change."

It's that simple, really. When someone says to me they don't know how I can be so devoted to my spiritual awakening into Divine Love, I always say, "It's easier for me to tend to this path (as a worthy work in progress) than it is to be miserable."

Misery is always the more difficult choice. Yet we choose it over and over. Until we don't. That's when something can change.

We can't strong-arm ourselves from our small mind out of misery. We can only continually choose the path of creating cohesion. The correct use of our free will is to yield to our Higher Wisdom, to Divine Love, and that takes practice. It's a muscle to build, and you have the rest of your life. Don't stop getting stronger because there is always more strength to be had.

How do you know when you're "there," you might wonder?

You'll know when you're fully awake. When you're in full union with your presence and Divinity. When there is no separation left to bring home to Love. Most of us aren't there yet.

I'd love to give you a wonderful tool for beginning to soften that defensive mode network and lowering of the wall. It's based in Heart/Brain Coherence and the work of the HeartMath Institute.

Coherence here refers to the quality of forming a unified whole, and a communicating system that speaks the language of safety, trust-building, cohesion, collaboration, healing, and wholeness. A scientifically measurable state characterized by increased order, healing, and harmony in our mind, emotions, and body.

It's an ancient state of being that you can cause and create for yourself in as little as three minutes. Your body recognizes this state because it's a natural aspect of the intelligent blueprint encoded in your cells.

Connect to this blueprint in three simple steps:

1. Touch your heart and shift your awareness from your head to your heart. Our awareness goes toward touch.

2. Slow your breathing down, which signals to your body, "I am safe."

3. Feel an elevated feeling. Research shows that one or more of the following four feelings work very well: gratitude, appreciation, care, or compassion.

This is an active process of breathing, and feeling the elevated feeling, and moving/keeping your awareness with your heart. This is going inside, from the outside world, to the motherboard of the body, which is the heart.

Something many don't realize is that the brain receives instruction largely from the heart. The heart perceives our feelings and perceptions (e.g. safe or not, anxious, well-being, tense), all these feelings convert to signals which go to the brain, which then releases chemicals into body. Almost all the perceptions are based on past narratives and stories which we will soon talk about how to change.

In the meantime, play with these simple three steps often, train yourself to regularly activate heart/mind connection and coherence, and you will begin to lower the wall. It's a way of self-regulating and calming your internal state so that the external, or outer, world (including your small mind) is less disruptive to your calm state of coherence. There's a few more ingredients in the wall-lowering recipe, but this is the place to begin.

Here's just a few reasons why you might want to play: connection and coherence create healing, resilience, deep intuition, access to subconscious, super learning and memory, increased immunity, expanded worldview, and understanding to be able to grasp and connect to your potential.

Imagine I am in front of you right now. I am bowing to your heart because you have recognized your heart call and are consciously choosing to mature and evolve yourself via self-initiation. It is the most potent thing you can do for your heart and the world. Literally nothing else is more powerful and potent and healing and world changing. Thank you.

Chapter 8: The Ticking of Time

"You will never find time for anything. If you want time, you must make it."

— Charles Buxton

What do you do when it seems as if there is more to get done than there is time for?

Five years ago, I was moving my offices and it happened to be over the year-end holiday at the same time we had family coming to visit. I remember having to sell office furniture that wouldn't fit in the new place – paring down to one treatment room from three – and of course, a couple other bits adding to the saga, such as our refrigerator breaking, and it being the coldest winter in history. Below thirty degrees in San Diego, and we have no heat. Contrary to many people's beliefs, it is *not* seventy-two degrees every day in San Diego – we have winters! And fleece!

A few months before, I'd learned about the theory of Einstein's time in Gay Hendrick's book, *The Big Leap*. He described how time is not as linear as we imagine. Rather, it's a circular and bendable phenomenon. What I learned is to put all the things that needed to be done in the

93

quantum field around me and to continue to do that whenever something popped into my awareness. The idea was to continue doing that, along with the practice of trusting the quantum field, the Universe, and the Creative Life Force, of which you and I are a part.

In my mind, I had nothing to lose. I'm a good gauge of time, and without question, there was not enough linear time for the tasks and timing of what needed to happen. It was from that desperation I decided to give it all I had.

I envisioned the field around me and put everything I knew needed to get done in the field (making sure I too was always in the center of the field, not separate in any way). I set a clear intention to the Universal Field of Infinite Intelligence that I didn't care how, or in what order, but that it all unfold in the right timing with as much joy as possible. I figured it couldn't hurt to add the joy part! Often (very often), my mind would get her underwear all up in a bunch about how much there was to do in such a short time. "I know, I know," I'd say, "but we're playing with this new thing." And with that said, I dutifully placed the things I was worried about in the field.

I noticed right away that I felt less like a victim of time and more like a partner. There was a noticeable sense of relief inside each time I consciously moved the "thing-to-do" from my spinning mind into the field.

I followed all guidance in placing ads to sell the furniture, finding replacement furniture that would fit the new space, organizing movers, and getting repair people lined up, all while continuing to serve my clients full time. Because all the "stuff" was not twisted up into knots in my body and mind, I honestly felt relaxed and found all the steps to be enjoyable. Whereas normally, I'd be resisting, complaining up a storm in my head, groping for the time it would all be over, and making myself and everyone else miserable until then.

Nothing was left undone, no ball was dropped, and everything unfolded magically. The perfect people showed up at the perfect time, every time. All the people that I sold stuff to were wonderful. Everything that was broken got fixed. We weren't found dead from the freezing temps encased in ice, San Diego style. OK, we had to layer with lots of fleece, but it all worked out.

I could literally feel the hands of the Universe orchestrating everything in perfect order. My only job was to stay out of her way, take the next step, one at a time, and keep partnering by yielding. By yielding, I mean not allowing my mind to yank the reins away from this dance with the broader holographic experience that was causing constant miracles every day.

Everything worked out better than I could imagine. And the joyful part was such a bonus. I will never forget this experience because it taught me that I am not, in fact, a victim of time. There is always plenty of time, and to the degree I am directive about that, that "plenty" is mine to enjoy.

Initially, I was so excited about this circular dance with time that can expand or contract per my direction. And because I had always, up until that point, felt like a complete victim of time, I took to poking fun at time saying I was going to "be the boss of time." This was the other side of the coin of feeling helpless, so not only did it balance out the duality so it could be transcended, it also made it more playful.

We remember that the lower human mind operates in duality, while the heart and the field she is connected to is not about duality, it's about wholeness. Something happens when a person decides to bring an aspect of duality to rest in her mind. It's about loving the duality free. There is a wisdom that can be alchemized from the creative tension between two opposing poles (duality) which generates a transcendent third energy of wholeness. It's the stuff of miracles.

Why am I telling you this? What does it have to do with your heart health?

Just about every person who realizes they are facing life or death lifestyle changes finds time to be a challenge. I'm suggesting that you play with time and insist that it serve you rather than being bound by it. As you do that, you'll come eye to eye with the magic of this dance. It will seem effortless in comparison to the old way. Just because it seems as if time is linear and limited, doesn't mean it is.

Don't allow time to be the determinant factor of your life. It's not. What is the determinant factor of your life? Your connection to life herself, and that connection resides beyond the confines of time. Thankfully. It's always available – and I do mean *always* – in every present moment.

Here's the thing about our lower human mind: When we are in that narrow point of view, it cuts off the body, the heart, the wisdom in every cell, and the entire field of infinite intelligence. Duality rules and life is harder than it needs to be. *But….* When we're open and connected, including the mind, body, heart, and Spirit, there is oneness, connection, flow, and wholeness.

Making a decision to live in this way is a rebirthing of sorts. It's a self-initiation that can only be done consciously and in connection with your Higher Presence, your Sourced Self, your Creative Life Force. I'm interchanging these nouns so your mind stays open and finds her favorite way of addressing this energy. It doesn't matter the address you use, it absolutely matters that it feels both intimate and infinite to you. It needs to feel vast and as close as your breath. It needs to feel like all of nature and all of you. Ask your heart, and she'll guide you.

Yes or No?

Have you ever said yes when you really wanted to say no? Honestly, I don't know anyone who hasn't.

One of the things I've observed in heart health is the need to only say yes when you mean it, and to say no when you mean it. For heart health to prevail, one cannot leave herself out of the equation. In fact, she must put herself first. Not as a selfish act, but as an act of keeping her own cup full first, giving from the overflow. Everybody wins with the full cup scenario. It's a core teaching of any spiritual path. Any other way is unsustainable, and there will be nudges to shift this into balance in the form of wake-up calls. It's actually selfish to not keep your cup full because then everybody loses.

If someone asks something of you and you don't want to say yes, or maybe you're just not sure but you feel pressured to give an answer, you'll do what most do and say yes to "give an answer" because that's what you think you're supposed to do. Consider saying something like, "Let me get back to you on that, I need to check a couple things first." Or some version of that. Practice saying those words out loud to yourself so they don't feel foreign when you say them to another.

Stop doing things that don't feed you, or rearrange how you do them if you can't step away. Be creative as to how you can turn everything into a form of nourishment.

Gathering your energy, plugging up your leaks, and calling back all parts of yourself is really important if you are to restore your health. Don't let false beliefs and stories tell you otherwise.

You're the only one who can manage your energy. Step one is discovering how to manage it to restore health. Step two is mastering it in order to thrive. Your heart knows.

One of my favorite ways to include the intelligence of my entire system in making a decision is something I call "light or tight." First of all, your system has a much broader view of all the components in space and time regarding any decision you have to make. Your mind doesn't have this view. She mostly references the past, which is extremely limited, if you think about it.

Since the intelligent field is everywhere, literally flowing in, through and around you, it knows your highest good on any given subject and communicates that to you through your body, usually in the vicinity of your gut and heart centers. It's your personal GPS.

When thinking of a decision you need to make, or something someone has asked of you, bring your awareness to that part of your body, and you'll feel a lightness or a tightness. Light means yes, while tight means not in your highest good, or no.

I suggest you play with this to get a sense of how to feel light and tight in your body. Start with things that don't have major consequence, so your mind doesn't try and hijack your dance with wisdom. When you ask your system, you'll get a clear light or tight, but then your mind will jump in almost immediately with logic, shoulds, and the discomfort of not pleasing someone else, which siphons your energy. You can't afford to waste your energy like that.

When I need to make bigger decisions, I give the same amount of focus to both sides of the decision. For example, I'll spend a whole day as if I'm making the decision one way. I'll envision going through the motions as if that's my decision, what I'll see, with whom I might talk, all the while noticing how I feel in my body. Then I do the same for another whole day as if I've made the decision the other way.

One of them is always lighter than the other. I always go with that choice, as it's never failed me. Ever. I've taught this to hundreds of other women who also swear by it. I've been doing it for so long, I don't even question it anymore. In the beginning, it was harder to trust, but it didn't take long for me to learn that when I went with the choice that made me feel tight because my mind made a logical argument for it, not only was it messy, I wasted so much energy to make it right. Not worth it.

Even something as little as my husband saying, "so and so invited us to join them next week." Instantly, I'll have a light or tight feeling. Why? Because my system knows all the components, including if there's time for us to do that thing with our allegiance to ease and flow (versus stress or tension and push). My system also knows if me saying yes to this invitation will be nourishing or not. I say yes to things that will return as much or more of what it costs me to participate. I choose to feel nourished by what I engage in, not drained. In this way, I can keep my cup full and contribute in nourishing ways, while being nourished. Win, win.

My mind is not capable of accessing this level of knowing. However, my heart – body intelligence which is connected to the Source of Life – is. And I've learned to trust her. She's like a GPS with real time updates, taking you along the perfect route to your destination. You inner GPS uses the language of feelings, and I've found that those feelings are felt physically as either light or tight.

This is a "permission to explore" thing. I've found that I must give myself permission to explore all of the stuff we're talking about, otherwise something stalls out. It appears that permission is the opener, the path-clearer, and the anti-stall element. We've been indoctrinated into seeking permission from those outside of ourselves. First it was our parents, then teachers, bosses, and slews of other authority figures. Giving yourself permission is imperative. Nobody else will.

Laurie Morse

How Much of You Is Actually Non-Physical or Unseen (But It's Still "You")!

Did you know that, to incarnate into a physical life, each of us had to squeeze the vastness of our True Nature, the unseen part of ourselves that makes up ninety-six percent of who we are, into the body and field you currently have? This is why I refer to a human being as a system that includes all the unseen space in between cells, as well as our unseen field. The point is that ninety-six percent of who you are is non-physical, and only four percent is the actual physical part that we see. Yet we place almost all our focus on this four percent? In the infinite wisdom of life, we agreed to squeeze our vast self into this sack of biology if we could sleep. It was arranged that sleep would play an important role in the harmony of the physical and non-physical.

Most of us are narrowly focused during our waking hours on the outer activities of our human life. During sleep, the non-physical part has some freedom to roam about the field, to move about the cabin so to speak, because it can be less physically focused. Sleep gives our overworked mind a much-needed rest. Sleep is the time our body repairs and restores itself. We've got to have sleep, and cultivating good sleep is as precious as gold.

During a particularly rocky time in menopause, I didn't sleep one single night for four months. I was miserable and remember driving to work wishing I could just be dead – at least I'd get to sleep if I were dead. It actually felt like I was dying. I could barely get through the days, cried all the time, and it felt like I was going crazy.

It took some doing to get sleep back on track, but it was worth it, because now I sleep like a teenager most of the time. There's a funky night here and there, but nothing like those four months of sheer misery. It's worth it to do what you need to do to sleep well. Good health rests upon regular good sleep.

The Eternal Moment of Now

An excellent devotion for our waking hours is staying focused in the present moment, as if it's your life jacket amid stormy seas, because it is! Here's the other secret to the present moment: it's the *only* place where change, healing, and transformation can happen. Healing can't happen when we're not present because there is a cascade of chemicals that are released when we're not present that activates a stress response and hinders healing. The opposite is true when connected to the present, a different cascade of chemicals are released that activate healing and flow.

Remembering to connect to your heart, slow down your breathing, and access an elevated emotion helps to usher us into present moment awareness.

Have you ever heard that most people live their life from past programming, bouncing back and forth from one past experience to another as if in a bouncy house? People will swear they are being present, but what's really happening is they are doing the thing they're doing all the while being *informed* and *influenced* by the past.

Not only do we freak ourselves out in the bouncy house, we can even go so far as to terrorize ourselves. Good-hearted people are doing this every day without even realizing it.

Meditation and mindfulness are great for a couple of reasons. First, it helps us practice bringing our monkey mind back to a single focus for the purpose of getting better at accessing the present. Second, it is only in those present moments that connection to life is available. Don't worry if you've tried meditation and it doesn't seem like it makes a difference, or maybe you noticed it did make a difference but it's too hard to keep up the practice – we'll soon be talking about a healing process that gives you the same results as meditation that you might like better.

Most of us are looking for ways to "self-medicate." Lots of people use food, alcohol, or any other number of not-so-good-for-us choices. Try self-medicating with beauty, and see how that works.

The Bane of Incessant Judgment from the Lower Human Mind

One of my teachers taught me how to banish judgment in the following way:

1. Be present enough to notice when judgment arises, which is basically all the time, on every subject, incessantly.

2. Upon noticing, envision a stop sign. I started envisioning with that, but I soon changed it to a ball of violet fire. I like the idea of the stop sign (stop judgment) but it didn't work because, in practice, I didn't want to see a stop sign. I loved seeing a violet flame dispersing and transmuting the judgment in my mind.

3. Immediately look at something beautiful. It could be the sky, a leaf, a tree swaying in the wind outside your office window, something on your desk, or in the room you are in.

These three steps change the well-worn brain track of judgment over time. It rewires the brain away from judgment toward beauty and presence.

This includes *self*-criticism and *self*-judgment, as well as judgment of everyone and everything. You may already be aware of this, but it's constant, this instantaneous judgment the mind throws out.

I have found these three simple steps to work for any form of judgment. Thus, we get to self-medicate with beauty, which I love. This medicine of beauty does a heart good. Beauty is a type of fuel for the heart.

See if your heart doesn't love regular doses of beauty all day long.

Chapter 9: Is Your Heart Broken?

"Know that only thoughts and emotions require healing. Consent to this healing. Allow it. Let the effect of the emotional thought-wound be healed by Love."

— John Randolph Price

Almost everyone I know has that closet that they shove junk into. I know I do. Sometimes that closet is real, sometimes it's metaphorical. Sometimes it's both. The metaphorical closet is the one we stuff our heartbreaks, betrayals, losses, disappointments, and devastations into. We put it away so it doesn't clutter our home and so that we don't have to look at it. We aren't quite sure what to do with it all, but we know we can't get rid of it. There's no Goodwill to call for a pick-up of unresolved emotions. By midlife, that closet seems to be pretty full for most of us.

For the longest time, I didn't want to open it because I was sure everything would come tumbling out and suffocate me to death. So I just kept walking past it day after day, hoping the door would stay shut even as it started bursting at the seams.

I've heard many stories of how the closet door eventually cracked or burst open, and it's always a catalyst that seems to be the precipitator of the door opening: a death, a move, a loss, a health crisis, a heartbreak…

Did you know there is a syndrome called stress cardiomyopathy, or "broken heart syndrome," which is a stress-induced heart injury, weakening, and even failure due to fear, loss, grief, and heartbreak? It's almost like a version of PTSD (post-traumatic stress disorder) to the heart, which ends up affecting the whole system.

It turns out the heart is extremely sensitive to emotions. It's been considered to be the storehouse of them. There is an emotional heart that overlaps or intersects the biological heart in mysterious and often surprising ways. There is a protective sheath called the pericardium that surrounds the heart, and in Chinese medicine, this heart protector is very much alert to emotions.

As human beings we were meant to experience emotions, process them, and then allow them to flow on through, rather than tie them up like hostages and store them for decades. There are some leading-edge visionary cardiologists who have been practicing for years and understand that approaching the heart like a machine that can be manipulated and controlled has limits. Cardiology has enjoyed great medical successes in the past hundred years with the advent of stents, pacemakers, defibrillators, bypass surgery, and transplants, but even these modern miracles are approaching their limits.

"A record of our emotional life is written on the heart. Modern medicine *must* be complemented with attention to the emotional life that the heart is understood to contain. A new paradigm is desperately needed that honors psychological and social factors front and center." This was said by Sandeep Jauhar, a cardiologist for two decades. This is what he has learned as he's tended his heart patients.

Another brilliant and renowned cardiologist who wrote the book *The Heart Speaks*, Dr. Mimi Guarneri, says, "Each heart has a biography, language, and method of revealing its truth, if we know how to listen."

Some of the language of the heart includes story, image, symbol, creativity and/or meditation, and importantly, being witnessed.

I've learned that each heart has a story to tell, and this story is literally dying to get out (like the stuff stuffed in the closet – trapped, unseen, avoided, and feared). It's in the telling of the story that emotions can move, flow, and heal. It's in being witnessed that emotions feel safe to become more than the pain. It's in the willingness to open the closet door that the alchemy begins.

When I finally mustered the courage to open my closet door, it was gentler than I thought it would be. Inner wisdom and guidance taught me that we don't need to relive and retraumatize ourselves with the emotional waste of the past. We just need to acknowledge, witness, and harvest the wisdom from the emotions and that can be done creatively, gracefully, and gently. I didn't suffocate and die – quite the opposite. After each healing, I was able to breathe deeper, felt more alive, and ultimately felt a sense of freedom and lightness I didn't realize I was craving. I noticed this to be true for every woman I've worked with, and now understand it to be true for all human beings. Stuck emotions want nothing more than to be brought to rest. This is an important ingredient in the recipe for feeling inner peace. Peace is a natural quality of life.

What I'm learning with each passing day is that the heart wants to be filled with light and love. It wants to shine, radiate, express and create. Alchemizing the dark and painful emotions makes room for the light, and while it can be hard and sometimes messy work, it can also be gentle and well worth it, because it's so much harder to live in the dark closet pretending not to be trapped. With each willing and conscious release from the emotional soup, deep healing is liberated.

Gary Zukav said, "By choosing your thoughts and by selecting which emotional currents you will release and which you will reinforce, you determine the quality of your light. You determine the effects that you will have on others and the nature of experiences of your life (including your health)."

Diet and Exercise Alone Just Aren't Enough

As much as the research recognizes diet and exercise as major contributors to reversing heart disease, it's not enough to facilitate coronary disease regression and reversal. Research also shows that managing stress and emotions is more helpful than even exercise. That's a big deal.

Leading science puts the heart as the center of our intelligence, decision making power, and memory. I think it's due to the ways in which our heart is able to connect to the quantum field. Ancient wisdom has always considered the heart to be the Seat of the Soul. Chinese medicine considers the heart to be the center of consciousness. It is a center of great complexity and power. Remember in Chapter 5, when we talked about why supporting a high level of nutrition is important? It's because the solar plexus energy center is the foundation of supportive power just under the heart.

In my view, if we aren't happy with the dance between abdication of power and abuse of power, we desperately need to get the heart involved for the right use of power. It's what the heart knows. To the heart, power is the same thing as Life Force, and there's nothing abusive about this power. All it wants is to heal, create, express, be abundant, and love.

We need to unlock, unchain, untangle, release, and open the heart center to express the treasures within. So far, those treasures are love, trust, grace, forgiveness, connection with others and life, courage, compassion, and an empowered, expressive sense of Self. These are the golden qualities and virtues we're looking for.

This is the gold that those stuffed, tangled, knotted emotions are blocking. We need those qualities and virtues in full expression on the planet right about now, wouldn't you agree? One life, one heart at a time.

Just a bit ago, I mentioned that the Chinese medical model considers the heart to be the center of consciousness. Deep contemplation of that is very revealing, in that consciousness is the state of being awake and aware of a higher reality, such as the Divinity within. That's what deep contemplation of consciousness will reveal to anyone, and if it doesn't, it's not deep enough yet.

One of the greatest of all heartbreaks is that Love, or our Divinity, has failed us. In fact, that heartbreak causes our heart to collapse. Human love has the potential to fail us, and it does for almost everyone at some point, but Divine Love does not have the potential to fail us. We mix the two up in our minds. If we are to heal our heartbreaks, betrayals, fears, anxieties, and losses, we must first reconnect with our Divinity so that we can know and feel from the inside out that in fact, Love has not failed us, we have simply had our back to it. If we don't start there, nothing will really change. It might look like there's change, but it's a sleight of hand.

Divine Consciousness carries within Itself the Law of Wholeness. When we are aligned with our Divinity, we have access to healing power.

As an extension of Love herself, Love is already whole. It can't not be. When I give myself the gift of being bathed in Love, in asking Her to show me the Divine Truth of my being, I have awareness of this wholeness. Then, the energy of my body follows my awareness. It's a Law of Energy that energy follows our awareness or attention.

We've been trained for thousands of years to place our attention on the "problem," which gives it the energy to increase. It's almost considered a joke, or harmful, to ask someone to take their awareness and place it on the Sacred Love that lives in every heart, which automatically withdraws focus and eventually energy from the problem.

I find the following quote interesting from William Tiller of Stanford University in *Healers and the Healing Process:*

"Through mind forces, one can create a pattern, and that pattern then acts as a force field which applies to the next level of substance. In turn that, force field is a force for organizing the atoms and molecules into configurations at that level of substance. That pattern of substance at the etheric level, then, is a particular state of organization and it has its own radiation field – its own force field if you like – and that force field, then, is a field for the organization of matter at the next level of substance – the physical level of substance. These etheric forces, then, bring about the coalescence and organization of matter at the physical level of substance."

Wait, What Did I Just Read?

Now let's unpack what this means.

Substance means every particle of energy seen and unseen. We can say substance also means Spirit. We said earlier that Love is the entire fabric of the Universe. Every single molecule. We can also say that Love is the substance and it organizes itself according to patterns. It moves from the mental body with a particular force field, applying itself to the next level, which is the emotional body (again, with a particular force field), to the etheric body, and lands finally in the physical body.

The pattern of Love is first, and this pattern is applied to the next level, which is our mental body. There are errors of thinking, such as "I am broken, an emotional wreck beyond repair (just look in that closet for verification), or wholeness is not possible for me after all, look at this huge health problem I have," and we even justify it by saying things like, "that's what happens with age," or "this is on both sides of my family, so it's just the way it is." As we "believe" that disease and disharmony in a human body is natural, then the pattern is created at that level and a particular force field is also created and impresses itself into the next level, which is the emotional level.

If we try and change or improve our health by manipulating effects (i.e. symptoms) rather than changing beliefs, which are the root of the symptoms, then we are digging ourselves deeper into a hole of disharmony. In the lower frequencies of consciousness (the lower human mind disconnected from Source), we can't expect much, except perhaps to bring some minor relief to the problem.

Only real change, healing at the root, which then reflects in the human form as wholeness, will happen by way of Spiritual Consciousness, a mind that is connected to the One Mind of Love, shifting focus from the false to the true. Anything less is a band-aid, like pressing the snooze button on your alarm. Sure, pressing snooze will stop the noise, but it's going to ring again. Nothing wrong with a band-aid when necessary. Sometimes it's lifesaving. We just can't call it healing.

I love this quote by John Randolph Price: "The body is maintained in wholeness when you live in and as Higher Consciousness. Open to this healing presence, the One Divine Power of Love, and be whole. Unite with Love and receive the inflow. Feel the energy as purifying light throughout the entire body. Disease is true only if believed. Shall you be healed of that which is real but really isn't? Know that only thoughts and emotions require healing. Consent to this healing. Allow it. Let the effect of the emotional thought-wound be healed by love."

Energy begins in the field of love, where all is whole. There isn't a need for healing there because Love doesn't mis-qualify its own energy. You and I being an extension of Love in physical form is where the "mis-qualification" of energy happens. We add our own false beliefs and mis-qualify our energy, which is part of what keeps them active. When we redirect our energy to what is real, which is Love, the "problem" can no longer survive on our energy or attention to it. In time, it is absorbed by our attention to Love.

Disease and disharmony are but shadows of wholeness, and shadows can never be real because they don't hold the real power of Love. Shadows can't *be* something real. Nothing cannot become something. Zero plus zero equals zero.

A physical body, as originally designed, is a sculpted pillar of light. Wow. I'm pretty sure most people don't see themselves as that. We must not limit envisioning ourselves as this pillar of light, which carries perfection and wholeness in its very atoms.

In my mind, what do I have to lose in this shift of focus? If I consider on the one hand the crazy ride that is managing a health problem in the current medical climate, and on the other hand the increase in chronic

110

health problems alongside the advancements of medicine, it doesn't add up. Don't get me wrong, some of the advancements are amazing and save lives, no question about it. But what about all the chronic diseases killing people in ever-increasing numbers? Those people are falling through the cracks without explanation.

It turns out that the Creative Life Force that flows in you, through, and around every particle of life is really smart. She's filled with wisdom, intelligence, power, and Love. There is definitely a way to access all of that. We can return our emotions and heartbreaks and exchange them for Love, just like returning an item at Nordstrom's. This is the alchemy I made reference to earlier. You might wonder how? That's what we'll talk about in the next chapter, the chapter I asked you to *not* skip. Before we go on, let's both do this lovely Heart Presence Practice together:

1. Place your hands over your heart.
2. Breathe deep and drop your awareness from head to heart.
3. Imagine a waterfall of light from the cosmic realms above gently flowing in through the top of your head. See it in your mind's eye, know that Love is always intricately woven with light, so see if you can feel Love filling your mind, heart, and body. If you feel anxious, drop your awareness into your heart. Only the head will be afraid, while the heart will trust Love.

You may love this right away, or you may need to do it in small bits to build trust as you integrate the light into your body. Don't give up. I use this to calm my system, to connect to Love, and to melt the energy of small emotional disturbances. The little emotional disturbances that crop up all day, not the big bad bogey ones that are hiding in the closet,

111

not to mention the heart-break that comes upon hearing a terrible news story, those need a more colorful medicine.

Now let's go talk about that medicine and your Creative Life Force.

Chapter 10: Creative Healing to the Rescue

"Heart Health is inextricably linked with the regular experience and expression of joy and creativity."

— Dr. Christiane Northrup

You now know the importance of good nutrition, of regular movement and heart health, you may have even had an inkling that emotional health directly affects your heart health. But what you may not have considered is the idea of regularly experiencing and expressing creativity.

Before you go too far down the rabbit hole trying to convince me you're not creative, allow me to stop you right there. There is no argument in the world, however strong, that would convince me you're not creative. How do I know that? Because if you're alive and breathing, you are a creative being. You are an extension of the life herself. Life or Source is a creator. In fact, she is *the* Creator or Creatress. Her core impulse is to Create. This very Creative Life Force is coursing through your veins and beating your heart right now. Therefore, you cannot *not* be creative. It's part of your nature.

Whether you are aware of or consciously cultivating your creative expression is another story. But you can't say you're not creative. Period.

Have you ever stopped to think that maybe your heart is asking you to create with her?

To be clear, I'm not talking about artistic talent here. I'm simply talking about your own personal expression, whether anyone else ever sees it or not. We create to be in communication with our Divinity, with our heart and soul. We create to connect into our personal medicine. We create to give long-held emotions a way to transform and heal. We create to learn about our true nature. We create to connect. We create to celebrate. We create to engage life. We create to know love.

Creativity is a way of being in relationship with ourselves.

Did you know that research shows that engaging in a creative process has the same benefits as meditation?

Benefits of creativity according to NIH study published in American Journal of Public Health February 2010 are that it:

- Reduces stress, anxiety, negative emotions, and depression
- Fills voids and distracted thoughts of illness
- Benefits immune function
- Improves medical outcomes
- Improves brain function
- Improves flow, function, expression of emotions, positive identity, and social networks.

"Through creativity and imagination, we find our identity and our reservoir of healing."
– NIH Study

You need your creative self, and it needs you. There are so many ways to be creative, it could fill another book. In our time together here, I'll make some suggestions, and I encourage you to explore and give yourself permission to discover the ways in which you love to experience your creative self. She's in there, trust me. Discovering her is half the fun.

I was one of those people, as is the case with just about every woman I work with, who said, "I don't have a creative bone in my body. I can barely draw a stick figure!" In my twenties, I tried drawing and painting and it was a disaster, so I quickly threw everything away and declared myself creatively hopeless. I stayed in that barren desert for over a decade when the impossible-to-keep-down Creative Life Force started stirring again. I was clueless to the stirrings.

In her Creative Wisdom, she inspired me to read *The Artist's Way* by Julia Cameron and take the twelve-week companion class. I had three different relationships with artists. I remembered that when I began studying Chinese medicine, it was considered a healing art, and I secretly loved the "art" part. Finally, I realized, "Oh, I want to be the artist!"

Sometimes it takes me a long time to "get it." I began receiving catalogs from the University of California San Diego, and it had an art and the creative process program that I read every time the catalog came (accompanied by lots of inner drooling). But I still didn't get it. I had vague thoughts about maybe going through the program when I retired, but my Creative Life Force didn't want to wait until then.

Then menopause hit, and one day, in a state of feeling lost and confused, another UCSD catalog came. As always, I flipped right to the program on art and creativity, while I was internally drooling. I thought, "Why wait until I retire? Why not do this now?" and in that moment, I finally gave myself permission.

It's a good thing because menopause was several years of rough seas, and I can honestly say to you that engaging in creative processes was my lifeboat amid those rough seas, being tossed about. Not only was creativity my lifeboat – it saved my health and life.

Today, I can draw more than a stick figure. I can wield a paint brush as a prayer stick, and I can bring anything to the "altar" of my journal page or canvas to be "altered." There have been emotional tangles that nothing else worked for except a creative process, and problems that only a creative process was able to reveal a solution for. There have been health issues that only a creative process could give me access to the personal medicine for. There is pain, sadness, and anger over world happenings that only a creative process can soften and help me understand.

If I don't move this energy and give it a way to flow, then it gets stuck. The longer it's stuck, the bigger the knots and tangles become. Then, they have no choice but to express themselves physically as disharmony.

I've been a healer for over thirty years, so I'm pretty familiar with the buffet of healing options. I love and honor them, but none compare, in my experience, to what a creative healing process can do for a human mind, body, heart, and soul. Bar none.

I believe it's because, when we start to become curious, and begin creating a relationship with this part of ourselves, it's as if we're curating and cultivating the Life Force within. Creativity facilitates curiosity which incidentally shares the same root as the word "cure." That's kind of a big deal.

Emotional Healing through Creativity

If our physical ailments stem from the roots of emotional disharmony, then stay tuned. There is deep healing with lasting impact happening all over the world, right now as we speak, by way of creative healing processes, so much that ten years of therapy could barely scratch the surface.

Remember in the last chapter, when we talked about how, when we speak the language of the heart, it can heal? That her trauma needs to be addressed in a language she recognizes? And that the language of the heart includes images, symbols, words, story, and witnessing? To heal, we must access the biography of the heart with compassion, which reveals pearls of wisdom and truth as the healing happens.

Drawings, colors, images, symbols, and words bypass the mind and give us access to parts of ourselves protectively held in the closet. Creativity brings light and compassionate witnessing to the trauma and pain for safe release. Creativity gives us a way to release false beliefs that constrict circulation and cause pain, and to reinforce flow and wholeness.

When we look at the colors of nature and her beauty, healing happens. Beauty is a potent form of medicine. Colors carry Divine Vibrations in their light. We can reinforce certain Divine aspects of ourselves using color intentionally when we create.

In fact, when we create with intention, healing is amplified, much more so than without intention. When we engage the heart, it's game changing. Many people come to their creativity with their head, leaving the heart on the sidelines. In doing so, what guides the creative experience is lots of self-criticism, self-judgment, comparison, and taking one's self out of the experience.

When the heart is the guide – and with practice – the critical mind settles down, and the heart plays. In that play, magic and miracles happen. As a spirit-centered woman, please be curious about this magical creative experience, and I promise you will never ever regret it.

Initially, the mind wants to run the show. She doesn't want to yield to the heart – that's normal. As you keep showing up and engaging anyway, inviting the heart to teach the mind it's safe, you'll make way for your very own personal medicine and magic to come forth. You'll also be able to create and rewire new neurological pathways for wholeness.

This is a muscle to build, and as long as you don't give up, your heart will reign. Healing will happen and wholeness will prevail. It's a treasure hunt that only you can discover. So what if it takes a year, or five, or ten? What else do you have to do but tread water in the rabbit hole of heart disease? Your Creative Life Force and your Conscious Creative expression is a life line out.

If grabbing that line meant a few blisters on your hand as you were being pulled up to the light of day, so what? Who would say, "Oh, no, thank you, I'd rather perish in this hole than get a few blisters that will heal in a short time."

We parent ourselves back to wholeness by showing the scared part of us that there are no monsters in the closet. There never were monsters, there's just some old junk to sort out. No big deal, we bring it all to our Divinity by way of the altar of creativity and allow it to be altered back to its original design.

Mostly our pain comes from knowing deep down inside we are a Divine Design, but don't know how to get to it, let alone feel deserving enough of it. Allowing the Divine Life Force to straighten out all the bent and broken places in our mind, body, and life is healing to wholeness. She happens to love doing that creatively.

We acknowledge an issue arising, and it wouldn't be arising if it weren't ready to be released. Up until now, we've been accustomed to stuffing it back into the closet. Now, you can safely bring it forward.

We bring it forward to be witnessed with compassion. Things happen for us, not to us. Everything that happens is an attempt to bring us home to Love. Why? Because there is only Love, and when its opposite is projected onto the screen of our life, it's a cry for Love. That deserves our compassion. The antidote to self-criticism is compassion. The antidote to judgment is compassion. Sometimes it requires some curiosity and creativity to access compassion, and that's OK.

Try to read this next part with your heart rather than your head. Each person's creativity contributes to the evolution of consciousness. If you want to contribute to the healing and evolution of humanity and the world, engage your creativity. Seriously, engaging with your Creative Life Force is the same as engaging with your Divinity. There is something in a human being's will to create the universe depends on.

You could start the most amazing non-profit to heal the world, but if that happens from a place of not being connected to your Divinity, it would not be as effective as if you never started the non-profit, but rather simply engaged your Divine Creative Life Force. That's how much your creative expression contributes to the whole. Your mind would argue that until the cows come home, but your heart knows it's true.

Getting Started with Creative Healing

This experience can be as simple or as elaborate as you choose. You can start with printer paper, a pen, and a couple of highlighters. Or you can get yourself a mixed-media journal and some watercolor pencils at your local art store or on Amazon. Or, you can be bold and get a canvas and some acrylic paints in colors you like and explore away. The paper, page, panel, or canvas is called a "substrate" in artist lingo.

You'll also need a journal that you can write in separately from your page or canvas. The combination of colors, images and some writing is inviting to the heart through the language she speaks.

Your paper, journal page, canvas, or wood panel is your altar. Your substrate is your altar. It's the place in the physical world of form, by your intention for it to be so, that you bring your inquiry and intention to be altered by way of the creative process you're engaging in.

It's the place where the energy held in your wounds and broken-heart are offered up to the alchemy and transformation released in the creative process and then woven back into the wholeness of your Divine Heart. The breaks and the cracks are where the light gets in to fan the flame. The Divinity in every person's heart is untouchable, perfectly innocent, completely connected to the Source of all life, and can never be broken. We fan the flame of our Divinity, like a bellows fans a fire on a cold winters night, with every creative process.

Every time you engage in a creative healing process, you are activating wholeness on the altar of your own creativity, you are weaving separated and unloved parts of yourself back into the fabric of your Divinity.

Grab a piece of paper or journal page and let's play for a moment. You need absolutely no experience to do this, by the way.

We mentioned "symbols" earlier in this chapter and one of the most obvious and well-known symbols for the heart is the heart shape/symbol.

You can begin by drawing the heart symbol on your page and writing in the center, or writing on the blank page first (see number two below). You may want to read the following four steps first and then decide how you'd like to play with the heart symbol. The thing about this symbol is that it gives you an image to look at that registers in your brain, heart, body, and Spirit that holds your intention and your healing via the creative process. It seems simple, but it's subtle and powerful in ways that don't always register consciously.

To get started, here are four simple steps you'll want to apply to engage your creative process:

1. *Inquiry:* Be curious when something is up. It wouldn't be getting your attention if it weren't ready to be returned to love. What is this feeling? From what story in me does it arise? Ask it, what do

you need? Living in inquiry regularly invites spaciousness and liberation. You can write these questions on your substrate and/ or in your journal.

2. *Intention and Invitation:* Your curiosity and inquiry will naturally lead you to an intention. If something feels broken, we want it fixed. If a well-worn emotion is running amuck, it's time to witness, release, and allow for transformation. Here, we state clearly what we are reaching for. What we would like that's usually the opposite of what we have. If we're frustrated, we would like a sense of ease. Be clear that you're inviting your Higher Self to this intention and creative process. Write your intention on your page, however big or small in whatever pen or pencil you're called to using, you can't do this wrong.

3. *Into Creating you go:* When you're clear about your intention, you've made your invitation to the Divinity in your heart. Take the intention to your altar. You can create as much ritual at this point as you're moved to. Light a candle, play some music, say a prayer, invite your Divine support, dance a jig, spray your canvas with water as a blessing. Write your intention on the paper or page, and then begin your creative process by drawing, painting, or collage shapes, make marks, lines, symbols, or anything that's inspiring you. You're doing this over your intention, you know it's there (you can take a photo if you want). Loosely hold your intention as you play, trust everything that comes up. You're not creating a gallery-worthy masterpiece, you're letting your Creative Life Force move energy in service of your intention. That's the point. The more you are soft and allow the process to be as playful as possible, the easier it is for energy to move. Do

not let any tension present declare the process a failure. There is no failure in creating. Practice and play with letting it be loose and enjoyable.

4. *Insights:* When you feel a sense of completion inside of yourself, meaning you feel a shift in the energy, you can either keep going or call your process complete. Then step away from your altar, take a break, grab a cup of tea, and change your channel of focus for a bit of time before going back for insights.

5. With your journal (and I like to have a cup of tea) sit down in front of your piece and ask, "What would you have me know about my intention?" Write whatever comes up. Don't censor, free write. It may be short and sweet, or it may be longer. It may come right away, or it may need to percolate. If you stay open to the insights and responses to your question about what it would have you know, it will arrive in right timing. This is a trust building practice. It's also a practice of receiving. We're so busy asking, even begging sometimes, pushing and grasping for answers, we forget to settle back with some patience and just receive. Divinity doesn't yell. She almost always speaks softly, so to hear her, we need to settle the noise and receive her. You might notice, however fleetingly, that you're actually being held like a mother holds a child by Divine Love herself. Keep dropping your awareness into your heart. Imagine your heart to be a chalice through which her Love and grace can pour. A healing salve for sure.

This process is the way in which image transcends mental barriers and moves into deeper places of our consciousness in order to gift us with insight.

I've done pieces where I get insights right away and others where I'll get a small piece to start, but I know it's not complete yet. I'll leave the piece out, and as I walk past the piece over the coming days, I check in and she'll give me the remaining insights in time. It's fascinating, I actually love this part so much. It literally feels like I'm connected and in a dialogue with my Higher Self.

It's as if the altar, page, or substrate becomes a portal through which communication can happen. Yes, it's part of the intention at the beginning, but see how that feels to you. Doesn't it seem like a portal opens up for this connection, exchange, and communication to happen?

You can make a pot of soup or plant a garden with the above four elements. Literally everything can be done with creative intention. It's a way of consecrating, or making sacred, everything in our life. As it should be.

A woman I know, Neesa, explained her reason to include creating as follows:

"I awoke yesterday with fresh eyes from the resting place of my bed. My entire life and sense of Self has changed.

"As I looked around my bedroom, I recognized how much has shifted because of the art on my walls. I recognized that I'd been 'marinating' in the transformational paintings surrounding me. I felt clearly in that moment that these images that have come through my paintbrush have been shifting my consciousness in the subtle spaces of my mental, emotional, and energy bodies every day.

"It may seem kind of obvious, since the creativity approach I've studied is meant for this. Yet something profound happened when I suddenly woke up to the larger picture of the changes that have been happening in my life since I began taking this path seriously. It's not just the experience of one painting, it's the ongoing journey of art as medicine that I grok now as so utterly profound.

All of this has opened up my consciousness in all areas of my life. I see it all in my overall sense of inner peace, joy, of clear life direction. It's truly amazing!"

As you are gathering your recipe for total heart health, it must include the ingredient of engaging your Creative Life Force. In doing so, you'll be able to creatively find ways to eat, move, release the old and false, reinforce the new and true, and awaken the intelligence in every cell needed to heal. This is the place where we access joy, a kind of happiness that doesn't rely on outside circumstances going our way. It's one of the most enjoyable ways I know of for creating cohesion between the head and the heart.

You are the artist in your life, don't give the paintbrush to anyone else. Your mind, your body, your choices, your life are all your canvases. What if devoting ourselves to creating beauty upon the canvas of our life is part of the medicine that heals? Honestly, most everyone feels a bit broken, but it's good to remember that even broken crayons can fill a whole page with glorious color.

Chapter 11: Truth in the Matter

"You never change things by fighting against the existing reality.
To change something, build a new model that makes the old model
obsolete."

— Buckminster Fuller

Often, while lifesaving, the waters of mainstream medicine can be rough. And expensive.

I've met amazing medical professionals with good hearts. It's the existing reality or system that's rough. The very things research shows that makes for the best healing, such as connection and emotional support, aren't part of a typical visit to the doctor anymore.

I had a woman tell me just yesterday that she has to write all the important points to ask the doctor because, "You know they don't have very much time, and I can barely get to ask two questions from my list. Plus, this doctor doesn't really know me, so he didn't really care about getting to everything."

I bet he does care, but he had to switch to a different channel when time was up. Schedules are tight. The demands are unreasonable for both the doctor and the patient.

Why is it like this? I've wondered for years, as it seems to have intensified and some would say worsened.

125

Over 200 years ago, when modern medicine began gathering steam and making great strides, I can see two things that happened. The doctors became heroes in what they were able to cure compared to the decades before, and that trajectory continued to build in momentum. Simultaneously, the patients put their bodies and lives in the hands of the doctors because they knew best. A dance of disempowerment on behalf of the patient.

In the later part of the twentieth century, patients began asking more questions and looking for ways to manage the chronic problems that medicine didn't have solutions for, and still doesn't, to a fair degree. There was a subtle pushback from the patient, and a desire on behalf of doctors to serve their patients. People and their health problems began falling through the cracks in ways that could no longer be ignored. The continual lack of solutions created the alternative medicine movement that continues today.

Enter large corporations, such as insurance and pharmaceutical companies, and here we have a system with disparate elements. The companies placing profit over people. The patients pursuing their health amid a system that does this, and the doctors caught in between. There's nothing healthy about this system. This is precisely why your challenge to become healthy is not entirely your fault.

That's the broad brushstroke that I've been in inquiry about for years and there's only one broad brushstroke that I keep coming face to face with.

What if it is so that an individual human mind projects its consciousness onto the screen of life? It would also be so that the human collective projects its collective beliefs onto the screen of life. We do that as a feedback system for what's in our consciousness. It's how the screen of life is designed to serve us.

What if the tangled, co-dependent, messy parts of the medical system (not the amazing parts that save lives every day, but the parts of the system that allow people to fall through the cracks, becoming less healthy rather than more) are to get our attention to take back our power as human beings? To claim our birthright and design of health and wholeness? To consciously activate and awaken perfect function in every cell?

I continually get shown this and have now for years. Remember the blueprint story? I can see how a system that profits from sick people doesn't want those people to take back their inner healer. It would certainly threaten their bottom line.

Enter scare tactics. Amplified conversations about the myriad of diseases that are sure to catch up with you. It's only a matter of time. Pharmaceutical commercials that all but manipulate a viewer into thinking that, surely, they "need" this drug – meanwhile the death-defying side-effects are spoken at such a pace, it's barely discernible. The media, the doctors, the patients, everybody is on board. The momentum and current are now strong. Profits are skyrocketing and people are petrified of their own health failing them. How can they not be? There's evidence everywhere.

Make sure you read the following words closely. I am *not* saying medicine is bad for you, or anyone. I am not saying you should stop receiving treatments and medication. I *am* saying that there is a far better chance that you actually heal, to the root of the problem, if you both take back your power, activate your inner healer, *and* traverse the medical system according to your inner wisdom. Then you adjust treatment and medications accordingly. Wholeness doesn't need to be medicated.

It takes a minute to develop that muscle. One must be willing to do that.

Nobody Escapes the Laws of Life

One of the most potent laws of life is that energy follows our awareness or attention. When you're consciously placing your attention on developing your inner healing capacity, you will have more encounters with doctors, practitioners, and treatment options (both mainstream and alternative) that support you at that level.

When you give your power to the system, you can only meet with options at that level. It's the law of life. This is where many people are frustrated, and they don't realize that they are half the equation.

Here's an example of not being empowered. Donna came in a few months ago and said, "My doctor said he'll give me three months to get my cholesterol down, and if it isn't better in three months, he's going to put me on statins." I asked her if she wanted to take statins for an only modestly high cholesterol value with good HDL numbers and not at all bad LDL numbers (she had been on them from a previous attempt to lower a not very high cholesterol). She said, "No, I hate how I feel on them."

"Ultimately, whose decision do you think this is?" I asked her. She thought about it, and I could tell it was very uncomfortable for her to even consider going against what her doctor said. Here's the thing, it is your body and your choice. Ideally, we work with health care providers, not as dictators but in partnership. We talked about how she needed to do her research and tell her doctor in three months what her choice will be. Which she did. With shaking knees, and all her mustered courage, she told the doctor she would not be going on statins. Then she took her heart health into her own hands and made a decision to up-level her heart health, which responded beautifully. She now lives with a sense of ease she thought was gone for good.

Choosing a Radio Station

For the sake of this point, let us say that there are two primary bandwidths or channels. The one bandwidth is infused with fear and suffering. This is kept active by our lower human/ego mind separated from the flow of life. We'll call this K-head. We know this station well because we've listened to it all our lives. It plays the most familiar music and tells the most familiar stories we know. In fact, we know the words to the songs that sing our stories by heart...not enough, unworthy, failing body, unlovable, underserving of wholeness.

This is what we know "by heart." Do you get it? There would be no heart disease if we knew our truth "by heart."

The other bandwidth or channel is the truth of your being. You are an extension of light, Love, and life. You can't not be. You have the Creative Life Force and Qi pulsing through your body now. The Creative Life Force is already whole and healed. It's impossible for it to be anything other than wholeness.

The motherboard for your whole, healthy, Creative Life Force is your heart. The intelligent message from your heart is to awaken to this Life Force that is your inner healer. It's a different station that plays different songs and stories. They are the songs and stories you long to hear because you know they are true. How about if we call this station K-heart?

If we want to hear K-heart better, we have to do two things. First, we have to lower the volume of K-head, then we have to raise the volume of K-heart. It's logical when we're talking about radio stations. K-head is the static that keeps us from hearing K-heart. Why do we keep listening to K-head when we have a better option?

Does it make sense to you that placing your awareness and attention on your Life Force will give you more life while placing your sole attention on your disease will give you more of that?

Some say this is magical thinking, yet thinking otherwise is a death sentence. It is my absolute knowing and experience that there is *nothing* to lose and *everything* to gain by choosing to align with the Consciousness of Life. If your focus is locked on to your disease to the exclusion of your inner healer and cellular intelligence with your heart at the helm, then the Law of Life can give you nothing more than disease.

I like to call this "minding the gap." There is your humanity with all its woes, and there is your Divinity in all its perfection. The journey, the practice, is to walk your humanity to your Divinity one step at a time. Every time something comes up that feels tight inside, it's an indicator that the gap is too wide. Love your humanity fiercely (you need your Divinity to do that), and reach for what you are learning to be true. Bring your woes to your Creative Self, and you will co-create ways to mind the gap.

Very likely, your mind will throw fits. Let her. Seriously, if she could have healed you by now, she would have. She. Does. Not. Know. How. That is not her job. Her job is to reason, be logical, and keep you safe. Healing doesn't live in the realm of the head. It lives in the realm of the heart. That's what your heart has been trying to tell you.

If you could have done this by yourself, you would have by now. Most of us need help in making changes at this level of consciousness.

As my sister said so eloquently, "That's what people do when they want to rise, they get help."

"Rise," in this case, is an interesting word. The bandwidth of life is above the bandwidth of suffering and fear. So we actually do *rise* in consciousness, lifting ourselves above fear and suffering to life.

This is where most people get stuck. They get a lift here and there and can sense, feel, and hear K-heart, but it doesn't last and they don't know how to get back there. They look for ways to get to it externally, but the elusiveness of that is painful. The longer this goes on, the louder the heart calls and the more difficult to manage the pain of separation.

Yet human beings are so creative, adaptable, and brilliant, we come up with reason why it's OK, all good, no worries. Just focus on the good, and my favorite, "So many people have it much worse off than me, who am I to complain. I have no right."

It's not about complaining though, it's about moving the dial to your designed channel. There is nothing that will help the "worse off than you" more than dialing into the channel of your Divinity, the channel that carries the fullness of life. If we don't do that, we're on a perpetual hamster wheel, spending lots of time, energy, and money, getting nowhere. It appears as if we're getting somewhere, our scenery includes our family and friends, and the goodness of life that gets through the cracks, and we call that good.

Life is not meant to be squeezed through the cracks into the bandwidth of suffering. Rather, we are meant to lift ourselves into Life Herself, which naturally sheds suffering because it's not a design of life. This is the meaning of flow.

Now, you might say, "If it's not the design of life, why is there so much suffering?" Good question. What if your suffering – not the whole world's suffering, stay with yourself on this one – as projected from your consciousness on the screen of life, is nothing more than feedback, a reminder, for you to tune your dial to wholeness? What if it's a heart call to your true nature? What if that's true? Why wouldn't you give it all you've got to explore that? Why wouldn't you look for the best guide to set you on that path the way you'd look for the best cardiologist?

Those are the kind of questions I ask myself over and over when I'm stuck. The question and problem always lead me to the answer and solution. But I've got to ask, or nothing truly changes.

Reversal of Heart Disease is what Must Be on the Table, Not Management of it

It's ridiculously expensive to manage a disease, let alone get out from behind the eight ball of it. The view of the rest of your life from the burden of expense and suffering isn't the most hopeful. Yet the greatest hope available doesn't cost a penny, only the cost of your attention.

The catch twenty-two is that there isn't a lot of extra time to dilly dally with heart disease. Not moving the needle could be deadly. I suppose that's why heart disease is the number one killer of women over fifty. Yet, you don't have to die before your time. Not if you're connected to life.

I have come to discover that healing to wholeness is an excellent Spiritual Path in and of itself. As I, and others I work with, embrace this path, there's an alignment of Life Force that comes together in such a way that healing is inevitable. Wholeness fills in as the light of Spirit

132

transcends the dense heaviness of what appears on the screen of life and in our bodies from the years of disconnection from Source.

Most women tend to think that, because they're spirit-centered (and that is very important and meaningful to them), "they're good." When I ask a woman what her spiritual stance is, I most often hear, "Well, I'm not religious, I'm spiritual." That's about the extent of it. I may be able to have her reveal a little more, like she does yoga, tries to meditate, loves nature, tries to be more loving and less judgmental, etc.

All of the above is happening on the K-head channel. And she's so familiar with being tuned into this station, it seems like there is no other channel. Your own mind is your biggest distraction and deterrent to solving any problem you have, including heart disease. Notice I'm not saying heart disease is "all in your mind," but I am saying that your mind is a fairly good obstacle and opponent, until she isn't.

Remember Marta from earlier, as she took herself through the seven steps of reversing heart disease? She said to me more than once, "I had no idea how isolated I'd become. Even though I have good friends, and people around me, I was alone on a small island in my own mind and I didn't even realize it until coming out slowly into the light of day." She said she would have fought to her death that she wasn't isolated, but women do that to a degree, even amid good friends and support. It's not about the people we have around us as much as it is the imprisonment in the mind. She thought she was *way* more spiritually connected than she was. Again, because it feels so familiar, it seems normal. Just because something is common, doesn't mean it's natural.

Marta knew she *could* take herself through the steps if she had to, although that wasn't happening, and she was wise enough to know it would be a steep and arduous incline on her own. Not to mention how expensive it would be to "do it alone." According to her, it was time and money she didn't have.

Her words, she said, "OK, I guess it's time to 'put on my big girl pants,' show up, and take care of myself. I can see that this is an element of spiritual maturity." She admitted that she didn't trust that she'd show up for herself all the way, too many excuses she had – busy, tired, overwhelmed, and her biggest barrier was that she was really scared. That's when she knew she needed support. Today, she says that she knows in her heart she'd probably be dead by now if she didn't get help to make the changes that gave her life back. She's deeply grateful that she used her dwindling resources to get my help. It saved her more time and money than she can count, as well as saving her life. She lives in an ongoing state of trusting the Life Force that carries light and Love, and she no longer fears every little thing she feels in her body. She knows in her heart she'll *not* die before her time.

Since she has successfully reversed her heart disease, she is vocal about telling other women to get the help and support needed, to set aside the resources, time, and willingness to show up to life, to show up for love. She'll go on as long as someone lets her about how love has transformed her mind, body, and life for the better. Her only regret is not doing it sooner, and that it took a life-threatening disease to push her. She's in awe of women who are able to do it on their own because, even though she's really smart, she didn't know how to get herself there, but she's made peace with that.

It is vitally important to your success to surround yourself with at least one person who knows the capacity of a human mind and body and expects the best from you. Otherwise, the current and your own mind will take you in the wrong direction. You need someone who is strong enough to not let your Truth slip away.

Anything and everything I've ever needed to up-shift has been with help. There's only so far I can get myself on my own. My mind will only give me so much, then she slams on the brakes. I've learned that getting myself headed toward change with gas in the tank requires:

- A qualified guide, teacher, or mentor
- Partnering with that qualified guide in a Sacred way that includes My Higher Self
- Major accountability (otherwise, I don't know what to do or how to do it)

Over the years, I've found this to be true for most people. Mostly because making significant changes is hard on our own. We just don't want to be uncomfortable or give up our habits, even when we know they're killing us!

If any of the words you've read inspire you to get whatever support and guidance you need to change the channel, then my heart is happy. There are way too many things you have to live for, milestones to enjoy, and the wisdom of your particular life lived to impart, if only to one other person.

There's not much time to waste on this matter. Because the *truth* is *in* the matter. In your matter. In every atom, there is light and life awaiting your connection to it. No matter how many times you've tried, you've got to try again because everything you've done up unto this point has prepared you to be successful in switching stations. Don't stop short of releasing the old songs and stories in favor the songs and stories of your heart. Most people agree that time is of the essence when it comes to life and death.

Reversing heart disease naturally liberates new energy, fresh Life Force that gives you a new lease on how you choose to live out the rest of your life.

Chapter 12: A Golden Invitation – Please RSVP

"There is a vitality, a life force, an energy, a quickening that is translated through you into action, and because there is only of you in all time, this expression is unique. And if you block it, it will never exist through any other medium and will be lost."

Martha Graham

I wrote this book because I have stumbled upon truths about healing, and it is impossible for me to keep them to myself. My sisters, women all over the world who matter, who have more wisdom than there are grains of sand on the planet, deserve to remember these truths about healing too. Women, when tuned into their heart, living into their wholeness, and expressing themselves as creatively as they choose, will cause and create some of the greatest transformations in human herstory. Ever.

You are one of those women. You matter. I see you. I bow to all that you are, and all you have yet to become. Let us not sell ourselves short, or our sisters short, or the world. There is no one person who can "save the world." There is only each one of us who lifts herself up in mind, heart, body, and Spirit. The saving of the world happens when there are more of us that have risen up than who toil in the bandwidth of fear and suffering. Let us remember these truths. This is how to heal.

Every heart that chooses truth is one who causes, creates, and curates a consciousness that reveals itself on the screen of life as wholeness, beauty, harmony, abundance, and love.

I want you to be able to say, "My heart is now healthy because I made a decision to activate the courage that had atrophied in the years leading up to being diagnosed with heart disease."

The insanity of the world now is nothing more than millions of insane people projecting their separated consciousness onto the screen of life. It sure looks and feels like it's true, it's just not *the* truth. I'm defining "insane" as craziness that results from operating as if not-truth (or false beliefs such as illness, suffering, fear, lack, and limitation) are truth.

When connected to Source long enough, truth is revealed. When disconnected, a form of insanity takes over in the mind.

Let's recap the steps you will take to rise up, access your truth, and heal your heart:

Step 1 – Your State of the Union

Here we had you face squarely toward the Source of all life for the purpose of getting you out of the strong current that is heart disease and the accompanying dire statistics. Heart health is not only possible, it's inevitable from this point of view.

In pivoting to your Source and dropping your awareness to your heart, you will discover you have everything you need to begin the reversal of your heart disease. In this developing connection with Love, life, light, Source, Creative Life Force, Spirit (you identified which address makes you feel the most internally connected, as well as connected to the Whole Universe), you see how it's not your "fault" that heart health is a challenge, and that failure is impossible because only the mind knows failure, while the heart, soul and Source of life does not.

There really is no place where you stop and Source or the Creative Life Force begins. Only to the lower mind is this even a thing. You have to build a solid foundation of knowing, inside your mind, body, and heart that this connection is real and true. Give yourself time, but don't give yourself a pass card.

This connection is what will allow you to be successful with the following steps in ways that have not been successful in the past.

Step 2 – Getting a Grip on Nutrition

You learned that to be whole, we eat whole. To be the light that we are, we eat food that carries light, color, and Life Force. Just about everyone who reverses heart disease, and you are now one of those people in training, increased their vegetable intake and decreased foods that gave no nourishment to the body that is a carrier of light and Love.

Step 3 – The Value of Movement

You were introduced to movement choices that bring you joy rather than having to push yourself to work out. You also learned how to increase energy.

Step 4 – Cohesion in the Mind

This is the fulcrum of the seven steps. To understand the science and implications of operating from a "closed system" in your lower human mind versus connecting to the whole, where you are invited to consider the role of Source as the true healer and immediately begin accessing your own inner healer. Game changer. There is no medicine more potent than this.

Step 5 – The Ticking of Time

Here, you learned how to create a different relationship with time. How cool is that? One as a director of time rather than a victim of time. This is powerful in giving you a new perspective on what you're able to get done on your heart health journey.

Step 6 – Heart Broken or Broken Hearted

What to do about long held fears, unresolved trauma, betrayals, and resentments create "knots" in the heart, diminishing healthy heart function? This is the place you learned what to do to release those knots and bring long held emotions to rest. In doing so, you have access to a higher energy of wisdom.

I want you to be able to say that your heart led you home to your true and highest Self, and if it weren't for the message heart disease was, you might have missed the most important message of your life.

Step 7 – Creative Healing to the Rescue!

The benefits of engaging with your Creative Life Force (statistically as powerful as meditation) are beyond the scope of this book, but we introduced image, symbols, and words as a language the heart understands and can heal from. This supports you in cultivating a deeper connection with your Higher Self as you discover the hidden treasure in your heart.

As you engage, you get to experience the magic of alchemy that happens during a creative healing process, in a safe and sacred space for releasing, evolving, and becoming the woman with a healthy heart, body, and life. This is true whether you have heart disease or not.

Here's what I know. Every human heart has treasure in it. It is the purpose of a life to discover this treasure. Part of that treasure is a powerful reservoir of healing intelligence in every one of your 37.2 trillion cells. You can awaken and activate this intelligence in order to consciously create a level of health and wholeness you may have stopped dreaming was possible.

I would want for you to take back your power regarding your health, because you now know the healing force that lives inside of you. From your empowered place, you'll make choices that support your growing wholeness rather than making choices from the fear of dying earlier than your time. These are two different places with two different points of attraction.

I want you to discover this treasure inside your heart and rock the second half of your life, living and giving from a full cup. I want you to mine the wisdom and gold that is this treasure and build your life with it, because of it. I want you to come to know in your heart that you are built from particles of light and Love, and to live from an anything-is-possible point of view.

I want you to come to these steps from the point of view that your Divinity knows to be true. That alone will change everything. That alone will render all past failures the perfect compost from which to blossom your being anew, even if you have to remind yourself of this a thousand times a day. I know I do.

I hope you resonate with this point of view so much that you can hardly sit still. I hope a light bulb is going off that, while it's nice to have the brilliant parts of medicine when you need them for an acute situation, you don't need it to prop you up, manage a chronic disease, or to keep you alive because you've connected so wonderfully into the Source of Life Herself. She is beating your heart and pumping your blood and you are one with Her.

What if you and I spent the rest of our lives tending this and creating a new model of healing? The way I see it, what else do I have to do but cultivate the one true healer, Love? I'm already playing here and would love to have you join me.

Acknowledgments

There is nothing that happens in an individual life without the "village." I'm so grateful to be surrounded by so many wonderful villagers!

This book would not be here if it weren't for Dr. Angela Lauria and her amazing team of editors, book coaches, and staff at Difference Press. Thank you Angela for the incredible team you've cultivated and for your devotion to getting messages of healing and transformation published. You are simply the best.

To those who invested in this book getting written and published, your trust in me is priceless. I'm so grateful that you said yes to being a part of this project! MAC, Leslie Padilla, Ken Kirk, Barbara Menard, Brenda Carlson, Kare & Bertram Furman, Mike Reardon, Sandy Groebner, Eileen Hunt, Kristen Makena, Lesly Perez.

To David Gruder, my beloved husband, who is such an amazing and supportive partner, your love is precious, and our shared love and life anchor me and fill my heart to overflowing.

There is a line in the book *Before We Were Yours* that reads, "I can't breathe in a world where you're not in it." I burst into tears when I first read that because I have two sisters, pieces of my heart, whom I feel that way about. Michelle and Kim, thank you for your undying support and love. To our parents, Ward and Jackie, who raised us well, thank you.

To my dear friends who are nothing but supportive, you know who you are.

To Shiloh Sophia, Intentional Creativity and its lineage, which you steward so beautifully, thank you for all you've taught me, all you are, and

143

all you do. For the Red Thread Circle, a community of creatives that are changing the world.

For the spiritual teachers I've been blessed by, who are numerous, some still here, some on the other side, all have lifted me. I would be lost without your guidance and lessons of truth. Deep bow.

About the Author

Laurie Morse is the director of Holistic Health Services in San Diego, California, a twenty-five year private practice dedicated to supporting wholeness (however imperfect) through natural medicine. She weaves various combinations of energy medicine, acupuncture, herbal therapy, hormone therapy, and nutritional therapy together with spiritual disciplines, Quantum Qi breath-work, metaphysics, and creative healing programs, including the companion program to this book, *The 7 Failproof Steps to Heart Health*, all in service of awakening cellular intelligence to HEAL.

Before entering the field of integrative health, Laurie spent well over a decade in the corporate worlds of finance and management. There she embedded into her professional foundation organizational development, teamwork, and corporate culture.

The balance of these two career paths has shaped Laurie into a grounded, yet spiritually oriented, author, artist, healer, teacher, speaker, and writer, enabling her to successfully work with women to reverse heart disease and live a long, healthy life.

She considers herself a guide on the journey, often walking with a woman over the "bridge" from where she currently is to where she needs to be to prevent a heart event and reverse her disease, so she can enjoy health in the second half of her life. She reminds each woman of the inborn golden treasure in her heart, and helps her mine that gold. It's creative alchemy!

It's Qi. It's the Creative Life Force. It's Intentional Creativity®. It's beauty and tea, and cats and color, and gardens and wine, and art, and Divine Mother, and books and her husband David, and deep belly laughs, and dancing and hiking, and friends and sisters, and excellent food, and healing and writing, and flowers and trees, and boogie boarding, and juicy connections that get her up in the morning.

About Difference Press

Difference Press is a boutique—style self—publishing service for clients of The Author Incubator, an educational company for entrepreneurs — including life coaches, healers, consultants, and community leaders — looking for a comprehensive solution to get their books written, published, and promoted. Its founder, Dr. Angela Lauria, has been bringing to life the literary ventures of hundreds of authors—in—transformation since 1994.

Thank You For Reading!
More Ways to Cultivate Your Heart…

Congratulations on finding your way to the end. If the recommendations in this book speak to your heart, I invite you to take a complimentary, one-hour companion video class. Here's the link to the companion class to this book:

http://aguidetonotdiebeforeyourtime.com/complimentaryclass/

You're also invited to join our Facebook Community here: https://www.facebook.com/CreatingAHealthyHeart

I'd love to hear how your journey home to Love is unfolding. When I talk with my sisters about their kids, I tell them I want all the details. I feel the same way about you —I want all the details! If you're not a Facebook person, you can e-mail me here:

support@CreatetoHEALStudio.com

Grateful for the legions of light and Love that hold safe and sacred our connection until our paths cross.

Be in touch. Big Love.